PRENTICE HALL
Chemistry

Lesson Plans

PEARSON

Prentice
Hall

Needham, Massachusetts
Upper Saddle River, New Jersey

ISBN 0-13-190416-7

1 2 3 4 5 6 7 8 9 10   07 06 05 04 03

Table of Contents

1.1 Chemistry

⏱ *2 Periods, 1 Block*

Objectives
1.1.1 Identify five traditional areas of study in chemistry.

1.1.2 Relate pure chemistry to applied chemistry.

1.1.3 Describe the evidence for the dual nature of electromagnetic radiation.

Vocabulary
matter • chemistry • organic chemistry • inorganic chemistry • biochemistry • analytical chemistry • physical chemistry • pure chemistry • applied chemistry • technology

Ability Levels

L1 *Basic to Average*
L2 *For All Students*
L3 *Average to Advanced*

National Science Education Standards
A-2, B-3, E-2, F-2, F-4, F-5, F-6, G-1, G-2, G-3

1 FOCUS

Build Vocabulary
After students have read about different types of chemistry, have them answer chapter review question 62. Discuss their answers as a class. **L2**

2 INSTRUCT

Connecting to Your World
Differentiated Instruction: Gifted and Talented
Challenge students to conduct research on the specialized areas of study in chemistry. **L3**

Use Visuals: Figure 1.3
Point out that pure chemistry, the study of existing fibers and how they are constructed, led to applied chemistry and the production of nylon. **L1**

Teacher Demo: Chemisty and You
Organize a slide show that highlights a variety of natural and human-created phenomenon. **L2**

Teacher Demo: Chemistry in the News
Have students scan local and national newspapers for news stories related to chemistry. **L2**

Targeted Resources
❑ GRSW: Section 1.1
❑ Transparency: 1.1 Connecting to Your World
❑ Transparency 2: Structures and Processes in the Human Body
❑ Go Online: Section 1.1

3 ASSESS

Evaluate Understanding
Ask students a series of questions to determine their understanding about the field of chemistry. **L2**

Reteach
Discuss how learning the principles of chemistry will enable students to better understand the modern world. Have the students make a list of some ways chemistry is essential to their lives. **L1**

Targeted Resources
❑ Interactive Textbook with ChemASAP: Section 1.1

1.2 Chemistry Far and Wide

 2 Periods, 1 Block

Objectives
1.2.1 Identify the main areas of chemistry research.
1.2.2 Describe some current focuses of chemistry research.
1.2.3 Distinguish between macroscopic and microscopic views.

Vocabulary
macroscopic • microscopic • biotechnology • pollutant

Ability Levels
L1 *Basic to Average*
L2 *For All Students*
L3 *Average to Advanced*

National Science Education Standards
A-2, C-1, C-2, E-2, F-1, F-2, F-3, F-4, F-6, G-3

1 FOCUS

Build Vocabulary
Explain the origins and meanings of the terms *macroscopic* and *microscopic*. **L2**

2 INSTRUCT

Connecting to Your World
Use Visuals: Figure 1.6
Have students research to learn about the materials shown in the photographs. **L1**
Discuss
Discuss the introduction and use of vaccines, antibiotics, and recombinant proteins to treat and prevent bacterial and viral infection, and diabetes. **L2**
Use Visuals: Figure 1.11
Ask students how the chemical pictured helps reduce the damage to tomato plants from pinworms. **L1**

Class Activity: Composition of the Sun
Have students explain how scientists can know the composition of the sun without collecting matter from the sun. **L2**

Targeted Resources
❏ GRSW: Section 1.2
❏ Transparency: 1.2 Connecting to Your World
❏ Transparency 4: Interpreting Graphs: Children in U.S. with Elevated Blood Lead Levels

3 ASSESS

Evaluate Understanding
Discuss with students the technological advances that were made possible through the study of chemistry. **L2**
Reteach
Have students suggest ways to classify areas impacted by chemistry other than the system used in this section. **L1**

Targeted Resources
❏ Interactive Textbook with ChemASAP: Section 1.2

1.3 Thinking Like a Scientist

🕐 *2 Periods, 1 Block*

Objectives

1.3.1 Describe how Lavoisier transformed chemistry.

1.3.2 Identify three steps in the scientific method.

1.3.3 Explain why collaboration and communication are important in science.

Vocabulary

scientific method • observation • hypothesis • experiment • manipulated variable • responding variable • theory • scientific law

Ability Levels

L1 *Basic to Average*
L2 *For All Students*
L3 *Average to Advanced*

National Science Education Standards

A-1, A-2, E-2, G-1, G-2, G-3

---

1 FOCUS

Build Vocabulary

Reiterate what the terms *manipulated variable* and *responding variable* mean, and give their commonly used synonyms, *independent variable* and *dependent variable*. **L2**

---

2 INSTRUCT

Connecting to Your World
Class Activity: Invisible Ink

Demonstrate a chemical reaction that reveals written messages which appear and disappear. **L2**

Differentiated Instruction: English Learners

Have students work with a partner to describe, act out, or illustrate the different steps that make up the scientific method. **L2**

Discuss

Help students analyze results that do not fit a hypothesis or vary widely from those of other students. **L2**

Class Activity: Researching Collaborative Science Projects

Have students research successful collaborative projects that involved a multidisciplinary approach to solving a scientific problem. **L2**

Relate

Have students examine a novel to determine how the author addressed the role of science, technology, and society in his or her era. **L2**

Quick Lab: *Bubbles!* **L2**

Targeted Resources

❑ Laboratory Manual: Lab 1
❑ Small-Scale Chemistry Lab Manual: Lab 1
❑ GRSW: Section 1.3
❑ Transparency: 1.3 Connecting to Your World
❑ Transparency 6: Scientific Method
❑ Go Online: Section 1.3

---

3 ASSESS

Evaluate Understanding

Ask students to choose an everyday type of problem and explain how they would use the scientific method to solve the problem. **L2**

Reteach

Ask students to describe theory and law in their own words. **L1**

Targeted Resources

❑ Interactive Textbook with ChemASAP: Section 1.3

1.4 Problem Solving in Chemistry

🕐 *2 Periods, 1 Block*

Objectives

1.4.1 Identify two general steps in problem solving.

1.4.2 Describe three steps for solving numeric problems.

1.4.3 Describe two steps for solving conceptual problems.

Ability Levels
L1 *Basic to Average*
L2 *For All Students*
L3 *Average to Advanced*

National Science Education Standards
A-1, A-2

1 FOCUS

Build Vocabulary
Remind students that certain key words and phrases in a word problem indicate the unknown quantity and its units. **L2**

2 INSTRUCT

Connecting to Your World
Discuss
Explain that memorizing facts is a relatively small part of learning chemistry. A person who succeeds in chemistry is a good problem solver. **L2**

Teacher Demo: Fit an Ice Cube in a Soda Bottle
Demonstrate several methods of transferring ice cubes into an empty soda bottle. **L2**

Discuss
Discuss using classification schemes as tools for organizing information. Ask students to describe classification schemes that they encounter in daily life. **L2**

Targeted Resources
❏ GRSW: Section 1.4
❏ Transparency: 1.4 Connecting to Your World
❏ Transparency 8: Problem-Solving Steps
❏ Transparency: Conceptual Problem 1.1: Running Errands

3 ASSESS

Evaluate Understanding
Ask students to suggest several ways to evaluate the accuracy of an answer. This will help determine student understanding of the three-way process for problem-solving. **L2**

Reteach
Have students try working in pairs to solve problems. One student will think aloud and the other student will record the process. **L1**

Targeted Resources
❏ Interactive Textbook with ChemASAP: Section 1.4

2.1 Properties of Matter

2 Periods, 1 Block

Objectives

2.1.1 Identify the properties of matter as extensive or intensive.

2.1.2 Define physical property and **list** several common physical properties of substances.

2.1.3 Differentiate among the three states of matter.

2.1.4 Describe a physical change in a substance.

Vocabulary

mass • volume • extensive property • intensive property • substance • physical property • solid • liquid • gas • vapor • physical change

Ability Levels

L1 *Basic to Average*
L2 *For All Students*
L3 *Average to Advanced*

National Science Education Standards

B-2

---

1 FOCUS

Build Vocabulary

Paraphrase *substance* by explaining what type of matter this term is used to identify. **L2**

---

2 INSTRUCT

Connecting to Your World
Discuss

Have students suggest possible reasons why mass is an extensive property and density is an intensive property. **L2**

Teacher Demo: Volume and Mass

Show students that air takes up space and has mass. **L2**

Differentiated Instruction: Gifted and Talented

Have students prepare a report about the fourth state of matter, plasma. **L3**

Use Visuals: Figure 2.3

Have students describe the arrangement of particles for each state in Figure 2.3. Ask what must be done to change the physical state of a substance. **L1**

Teacher Demo: States of Chocolate

Heat chocolate to show three states of matter. **L2**

Targeted Resources

❑ GRSW: Section 2.1
❑ Transparency: 2.1 Connecting to Your World
❑ Transparency 11: Comparing Solids, Liquids, and Gases
❑ Go Online: Section 2.1

---

3 ASSESS

Evaluate Understanding

Ask students to explain how burning a candle involves three states of matter. **L2**

Reteach

Explain that no two substances can have the same melting point, boiling point, and density. Provide students with descriptions of particular physical properties and have them refer to Table 2.1 to identify the substance. **L1**

Targeted Resources

❑ Interactive Textbook with ChemASAP: Section 2.1

2.2 Mixtures

2 Periods, 1 Block

Objectives

2.2.1 **Categorize** a sample of matter as a substance or a mixture.

2.2.2 **Distinguish** between homogeneous and heterogeneous samples of matter.

2.2.3 **Describe** two ways that components of mixtures can be separated.

Vocabulary

mixture • heterogeneous mixture
• homogeneous mixture • solution • phase
• filtration • distillation

Ability Levels
L1 *Basic to Average*
L2 *For All Students*
L3 *Average to Advanced*

National Science Education Standards
A-1

---

1 FOCUS

Build Vocabulary
Have students write sentences using words that contain the roots *hetero-* and *homo-*. **L2**

---

2 INSTRUCT

Connecting to Your World
Discuss
Show students an example of a mixture to help guide them in a discussion about the differences between the properties of a mixture and those of a substance. **L2**

Differentiated Instruction: English Learners
Have students create a glossary that includes their definition of chapter terms written in English and in their native language. **L1**

Teacher Demo: Metallic Breakfast
In order to observe the separation of iron fillings from iron-fortified breakfast cereal, have students use a magnetic stirrer to mix distilled water with cereal. Explain that stomach acid will change the iron into a form that the body can use. **L2**

Use Visuals: Figure 2.8
Review the distillation process while students look at Figure 2.8. Ask students what might be an advantage to having a long condenser. **L1**

Targeted Resources
❏ GRSW: Section 2.2
❏ Transparency: 2.2 Connecting to Your World
❏ Transparency: Conceptual Problem 2.1: Separating a Heterogeneous Mixture
❏ Transparency 14: Distillation Apparatus

---

3 ASSESS

Evaluate Understanding
Have students outline the methods for separating components of homogeneous and heterogeneous mixtures and of solutions. **L2**

Reteach
Set up lab stations with examples of elements, mixtures, and compounds. Then have partners classify each sample as a substance, homogeneous mixture, or heterogeneous mixture. **L1**

Targeted Resources
❏ Interactive Textbook with ChemASAP: Section 2.2

2.3 Elements and Compounds

4 Periods, 2 Blocks

Objectives

2.3.1 Explain the difference between an element and a compound.

2.3.2 Distinguish between a substance and a mixture.

2.3.3 Identify the chemical symbols of common elements, and **name** common elements, given their symbols.

Vocabulary

element • compound • chemical change • chemical symbol

Ability Levels
L1 *Basic to Average*
L2 *For All Students*
L3 *Average to Advanced*

National Science Education Standards
A-1, B-2, B-3, G-3

1 FOCUS

Build Vocabulary
Ask students to picture in their minds the meaning of *element* and *compound*. Then have them describe their images. **L2**

2 INSTRUCT

Connecting to Your World
Teacher Demo: Heating Sugar
Separate sugar into an element (carbon) and a compound (water). **L2**

Differentiated Instruction: Gifted and Talented
Have students research what conditions are necessary to decompose water using heat. Encourage them to find out why this method might not be used regularly. **L3**

Use Visuals: Figure 2.11
Ask students why the gold ornament is considered a mixture. Ask if compounds can be separated into their component elements by physical processes. **L1**

Class Activity: Substances
Start filling in a two-column chart with items grouped by a predetermined factor. Have students continue the chart until they recognize a uniform and definite composition. **L2**

Relate
Ask each student to choose an element with a symbol that doesn't seem to match its name, then research the origin of the symbol. **L2**

Targeted Resources
❑ GRSW: Section 2.3
❑ Transparency: 2.3 Connecting to Your World
❑ Transparency 16: Classifying Matter
❑ Transparency: Conceptual Problem 2.2: Classifying Materials
❑ Go Online: Section 2.3

3 ASSESS

Evaluate Understanding
Ask students to use their own words to explain the difference between an element and a compound. **L2**

Reteach
Help students relate abstract chemical symbols to real substances by setting up a display of elements. **L1**

Targeted Resources
❑ Interactive Textbook with ChemASAP: Section 2.3

2.4 Chemical Reactions

2 Periods, 1 Block

Objectives

2.4.1 Describe what happens during a chemical change.

2.4.2 Identify four clues that a chemical change has taken place, and **recognize** that the composition of matter has changed in each.

2.4.3 Apply the law of conservation of mass to chemical reactions.

Vocabulary

chemical property • chemical reaction • reactant • product • precipitate • law of conservation of mass

Ability Levels
L1 *Basic to Average*
L2 *For All Students*
L3 *Average to Advanced*

National Science Education Standards

B-2, B-3, G-2

---

1 FOCUS

Build Vocabulary

Have students build a concept map using some of the section terms. **L2**

---

2 INSTRUCT

Connecting to Your World
Use Visuals: Figure 2.13

Point out that in Figure 2.13 a chemical reaction is occurring when heat combines iron and sulfur in a compound. Ask students to write a word equation for this reaction. **L1**

Teacher Demo: Identifying a Chemical Change

Perform several procedures and have students identify the clue for chemical change in each. **L2**

Targeted Resources

❏ Laboratory Manual: Labs 2, 3
❏ Small-Scale Chemistry Lab Manual: Lab 2
❏ Laboratory Practical: 2-1
❏ GRSW: Section 2.4
❏ Transparency: 2.4 Connecting to Your World
❏ Transparency 19: Conservation of Mass
❏ Go Online: Section 2.4

---

3 ASSESS

Evaluate Understanding

Ask students to write shorthand equations for the reactions in the Teacher Demo Identifying a Chemical Change. **L2**

Reteach

On the board write an equation for magnesium and oxygen changing to magnesium oxide. Ask students to explain how mass is conserved in this reaction. **L1**

Targeted Resources

❏ Interactive Textbook with ChemASAP: Section 2.4

3.1 Measurements and Their Uncertainty

2 Periods, 1 Block

Objectives

3.1.1 Convert measurements to scientific notation.

3.1.2 Distinguish among the accuracy, precision, and error of a measurement.

3.1.3 Identify the number of significant figures in a measurement and in the result of a calculation.

Vocabulary

measurement • scientific notation • accuracy • precision • accepted value • experimental value • error • percent error • significant figures

Ability Levels
L1 *Basic to Average*
L2 *For All Students*
L3 *Average to Advanced*

National Science Education Standards
A-1, A-2, G-2

1 FOCUS

Build Vocabulary

Have students write definitions for *accurate* and *precise*, comparing these to the text's definitions of *accuracy* and *precision*. **L2**

2 INSTRUCT

Connecting to Your World
Use Visuals: Figure 3.1

Have students study the caption for Figure 3.1 and ask them to find the relationship between the exponent and the number of places the decimal point has to move. **L1**

Class Activity: Precision and Accuracy

Have students compare measurements for mass of an object using a triple-beam balance. **L2**

Discuss

Ask what the meanings of *positive error* and *negative error* are. Explain that the absolute value of the error is a positive value that describes the difference between the measured value and the accepted value. **L2**

Differentiated Instruction: Less Proficient Readers

Have students use their own words to describe the rules for determining the number of significant digits. **L1**

Quick Lab: *Accuracy and Precision* **L2**

Targeted Resources

❑ Small-Scale Chemistry Lab Manual: Lab 5
❑ GRSW: Section 3.1
❑ Transparency: 3.1 Connecting to Your World
❑ Transparency 21: Accuracy and Precision
❑ Transparency: Conceptual Problem 3.1: Counting Significant Figures in Measurement

3 ASSESS

Evaluate Understanding

Provide students with several sets of measurements. Ask them which is the most precise if these sets were made of the boiling point of a liquid under similar conditions. **L2**

Reteach

Review the method of correctly recording the number of significant figures in a measurement.

Then have students convert each measurement in Figure 3.5 into a scientific notation. **L1**

Targeted Resources

❑ Interactive Textbook with ChemASAP: Section 3.1

3.2 The International System of Units (SI)

2 Periods, 1 Block

Objectives

3.2.1 List SI units of measurement and common SI prefixes.

3.2.2 Distinguish between the mass and weight of an object.

3.2.3 Convert between the Celsius and Kelvin temperature scales.

Vocabulary

International System of Units (SI) • meter (m) • liter (L) • weight • kilogram (kg) • gram (g) • temperature • Celsius scale • Kelvin scale • absolute zero • energy • joule (J) • calorie (cal)

Ability Levels

L1 *Basic to Average*
L2 *For All Students*
L3 *Average to Advanced*

National Science Education Standards

A-1, A-2, G-2

1 FOCUS

Build Vocabulary

Have students use prior knowledge to predict the meaning of each of the following SI prefixes: *deci-*, *centi-*, and *milli-*. **L2**

2 INSTRUCT

Connecting to Your World
Discuss

Even though it is the only country without the metric system as its official measurement method, ask students what are some ways the United States uses the metric system. **L2**

Use Visuals: Table 3.2

Explain that SI prefixes are always in increments of ten. Ask students what *kilo-* means and how it is represented in scientific notation. **L1**

Class Activity: Mass of a Penny

Have students weigh groups of pennies and calculate the average mass of a penny. Then have them plot the average mass versus the year it was minted. **L2**

Targeted Resources

❏ Laboratory Manual: Lab 4
❏ Small-Scale Chemistry Lab Manual: Labs 3, 4, 5
❏ GRSW: Section 3.2
❏ Transparency: 3.2 Connecting to Your World
❏ Transparency 28: SI Base Units
❏ Transparency: Sample Problem 3.4: Converting Between Temperature Scales
❏ Go Online: Section 3.2

3 ASSESS

Evaluate Understanding

Have students match the appropriate magnitude and SI unit with various items. **L2**

Reteach

Review SI base units, pronunciations of derived units, and the use of the prefixes to determine the numerical relationships between the base unit and the derived units. **L2**

Targeted Resources

❏ Interactive Textbook with ChemASAP: Section 3.2

3.3 Conversion Problems

⏲ *2 Periods, 1 Block*

Objectives

3.3.1 **Construct** conversion factors from equivalent measurements.

3.3.2 **Apply** the techniques of dimensional analysis to a variety of conversion problems.

3.3.3 **Solve** problems by breaking the solution into steps.

3.3.4 **Convert** complex units, using dimensional analysis.

Vocabulary

conversion factor • dimensional analysis

Ability Levels
- **L1** *Basic to Average*
- **L2** *For All Students*
- **L3** *Average to Advanced*

National Science Education Standards

A-1, A-2

---

1 FOCUS

Build Vocabulary

Have students use their own words to define the vocabulary terms. **L2**

---

2 INSTRUCT

Connecting to Your World
Use Visuals: Figure 3.11

Have students look at the figure showing two parts of a conversion factor. Ask them to name the two parts that every measurement has. Then point out that every conversion factor must contain two numbers and two units. **L1**

Class Activity: Expanding a Recipe

Have students rewrite a recipe to feed six times the serving size given. They need to convert the units to larger ones instead of just using six of the given units. **L2**

Differentiated Instruction: Less Proficient Readers

Remind students to look for clues, such as *how much* or *what is*, that will let them know what the unknown quantity and its units are in word problems. **L1**

Quick Lab: *Dimensional Analysis* **L2**

Targeted Resources

❏ Laboratory Manual: Lab 4
❏ Small-Scale Chemistry Lab Manual: Lab 5
❏ GRSW: Section 3.3
❏ Transparency: 3.3 Connecting to Your World
❏ Transparency 32: A Conversion Factor
❏ Transparency: Sample Problem 3.5: Using Dimensional Analysis

---

3 ASSESS

Evaluate Understanding

Have students explain the relationship between the numerator and the denominator of any measurement conversion factor. **L2**

Reteach

Model the conversion of 2 L to 2000 mL. Explain that the answer can be checked by observing that the smaller unit has the larger number. **L2**

Targeted Resources

❏ Interactive Textbook with ChemASAP: Section 3.3

3.4 Density

⏱ *2 Periods, 1 Block*

Objectives
3.4.1 Calculate the density of a material from experimental data.

3.4.2 Describe how density varies with temperature.

Vocabulary
density

Ability Levels
L1 *Basic to Average*
L2 *For All Students*
L3 *Average to Advanced*

National Science Education Standards
A-1, A-2, E-2, G-1

1 FOCUS

Build Vocabulary
After students read the key concept, have them infer the meaning of *extensive property*. **L2**

2 INSTRUCT

Connecting to Your World
Teacher Demo: Density Calculations
Show students how to calculate density from a mass–volume graph. **L2**

Differentiated Instruction: Less Proficient Readers
Have students write definitions of density in English and, if appropriate, in a native language. Have them find photos of objects containing substances from Table 3.6. **L2**

Discuss
Describe how the density equation can be used to determine the mass or volume of an object. **L2**

Relate
Explain how a Galileo thermometer measures temperature. **L2**

Teacher Demo: The Hydrometer
Show students how a hydrometer measures the specific gravity of a liquid. **L2**

Targeted Resources
❑ Laboratory Manual: Lab 4
❑ Small-Scale Chemistry Lab Manual: Lab 5
❑ Laboratory Practical: 3-1, 3-2
❑ GRSW: Section 3.4
❑ Transparency: 3.4 Connecting to Your World
❑ Transparency 39: Comparing Densities of Lithium, Water, and Lead
❑ Transparency 40: Densities of Some Common Materials
❑ Transparency: Sample Problem 3.10: Calculating Density
❑ Go Online: Section 3.4

3 ASSESS

Evaluate Understanding
Ask what the most common units for expressing the density of a substance are. Then ask how density can be used to determine whether a metal washer is aluminum or zinc. **L2**

Reteach
Show an alternate way of writing the density equation. Ask students to find the thickness of a square piece of aluminum using this equation. **L2**

Targeted Resources
❑ Interactive Textbook with ChemASAP: Section 3.4

4.1 Defining the Atom

2 Periods, 1 Block

Objectives
4.1.1 Describe Democritus's ideas about atoms.
4.1.2 Explain how Dalton improved earlier atomic ideas.
4.1.3 Understand that special instruments are necessary to observe individual atoms.

Vocabulary
atom • Dalton's atomic theory

Ability Levels
L1 *Basic to Average*
L2 *For All Students*
L3 *Average to Advanced*

National Science Education Standards
A-2, B-1, B-2, B-3, E-2, G-2, G-3

1 FOCUS

Build Vocabulary
Discuss what a scientific theory is. **L2**

2 INSTRUCT

Connecting to Your World
Use Visuals: Figure 4.1
Explain that globes are models. Ask why people use models. Have students discuss models they have used. **L1**

Discuss
Explain that John Dalton's work became the basis for modern atomic theory. Discuss how the atomic theory has been tested and refined over time. **L2**

Use Visuals: Figure 4.2
Point out the particles that could be molecules of water. Ask how many atoms of A and B form a molecule of water. Ask if mixtures, as shown in Figure 4.2, always lead to compounds. **L1**

Targeted Resources
❑ GRSW: Section 4.1
❑ Transparency: 4.1 Connecting to Your World
❑ Transparency 44: Dalton's Atomic Theory

3 ASSESS

Evaluate Understanding
Have students evaluate and criticize statements according to Dalton's theory. **L2**

Reteach
Review Dalton's model of the atoms. Discuss how STM could be used to support or disprove Dalton's theory. **L1**

Targeted Resources
❑ Interactive Textbook with ChemASAP: Section 4.1

4.2 Structure of the Nuclear Atom

2 Periods, 1 Block

Objectives
4.2.1 Identify three types of subatomic particles.
4.2.2 Describe the structure of atoms according to the Rutherford model.

Vocabulary
electrons • cathode ray • protons • neutrons • nucleus

Ability Levels
L1 *Basic to Average*
L2 *For All Students*
L3 *Average to Advanced*

National Science Education Standards
A-1, A-2, B-1, B-4, G-2, G-3

---

1 FOCUS

Build Vocabulary
Have students think of words that start with the same word parts as *neutron, electron,* and *proton.*
L2

---

2 INSTRUCT

Connecting to Your World
Teacher Demo: Using a Cathode-Ray Tube
Demonstrate a cathode-ray tube in class. Review its components and discuss the connection to television picture tubes and computer monitors.
L2

Use Visuals: Table 4.1
Have students compare the masses and charges of the three elementary particles shown in Table 4.1. **L1**

Class Activity: Atomic Model Timeline
Have students create a timeline that traces the development of the atomic model. **L2**

Differentiated Instruction: Gifted and Talented
Have students use the Internet or library to find the original papers for the discoveries described in this chapter and write a report on what they have learned. **L3**

Discuss
Discuss how small the nucleus is compared to the entire atom. **L2**
Quick Lab: *Using Inference: The Black Box* **L2**

Targeted Resources
❏ Laboratory Manual: Lab 5
❏ Laboratory Practical: 5-1
❏ GRSW: Section 4.2
❏ Transparency: 4.2 Connecting to Your World
❏ Transparency 46: Properties of Subatomic Particles
❏ Transparency 47: Rutherford's Gold-Foil Experiment
❏ Go Online: Section 4.2

---

3 ASSESS

Evaluate Understanding
Have students describe how the discoveries of Thompson, Millikan, and Rutherford led to the current understanding of atomic structure. **L2**

Reteach
Using Table 4.1, have students create their own tables or diagrams to compare electrons, protons, and neutrons. **L1**

Targeted Resources
❏ Interactive Textbook with ChemASAP: Section 4.2

4.3 Distinguishing Between Atoms

2 Periods, 1 Block

Objectives

4.3.1 Explain what makes elements and isotopes different from each other.

4.3.2 Calculate the number of neutrons in an atom.

4.3.3 Calculate the atomic mass of an element.

Vocabulary

atomic number • mass number • isotopes • atomic mass unit (amu) • atomic mass • periodic table • period • group

Ability Levels

L1 *Basic to Average*
L2 *For All Students*
L3 *Average to Advanced*

National Science Education Standards

A-1, A-2, B-1, B-2, G-1, G-2

1 FOCUS

Build Vocabulary

Have students build a concept map that links and relates the vocabulary for this section. **L2**

2 INSTRUCT

Connecting to Your World
Discuss

Discuss why the mass number of an element is defined as the number of protons and neutrons. Ask students how to find the number of neutrons in an atom. **L2**

Differentiated Instruction: Less Proficient Readers

Have students make a list of familiar elements and describe at least one use for each element. **L1**

Class Activity: Finding Isotopes

Have students research an isotope of an element that has a practical use, such as carbon-14, americium-241, iodine-1331, and cobalt-60. **L2**

Discuss

Ask students why isotopes of an element are chemically the same. **L2**

Use Visuals: Table 4.3

Have students study Table 4.3. Explain that the average atomic masses listed are based on the masses of stable isotopes and their percent abundance in Earth's crust. **L1**

Targeted Resources

❑ Small-Scale Chemistry Lab Manual: Lab 6
❑ GRSW: Section 4.3
❑ Transparency: 4.3 Connecting to Your World
❑ Transparency 49: Atoms of the First Ten Elements
❑ Transparency: Conceptual Problem 4.1: Understanding Atomic Number
❑ Transparency: Sample Problem 4.1: Determining the Composition of an Atom
❑ Transparency 52: Neon Isotopes
❑ Go Online: Section 4.3

3 ASSESS

Evaluate Understanding

Give students symbols for isotopes of an element. Ask students what the superscripts and subscripts refer to and the differences between the atoms shown. **L2**

Reteach

Review the concept of weighted averages. Have students work through various calculations. **L1**

Targeted Resources

❑ Interactive Textbook with ChemASAP: Section 4.3

5.1 Models of the Atom

4 Periods, 2 Blocks

Objectives

5.1.1 Identify inadequacies in the Rutherford atomic model.

5.1.2 Identify the new assumption in the Bohr model of the atom.

5.1.3 Describe the energies and positions of electrons according to the quantum mechanical model.

5.1.4 Describe how the shapes of orbitals at different sublevels differ.

Vocabulary

energy levels • quantum • quantum mechanical model • atomic orbital

Ability Levels

L1 *Basic to Average*
L2 *For All Students*
L3 *Average to Advanced*

National Science Education Standards

A-2, B-1, B-2, B-3, E-2, G-3

1 FOCUS

Build Vocabulary
Discuss the origin of the word *orbital*. **L2**

2 INSTRUCT

Connecting to Your World
Relate
Discuss how the evolution of an item, such as the car, compares to the development of the atomic model. **L2**

Teacher Demo: Quantized Energy
Use a trumpet or trombone to show how the instrument accepts quantized packages of energy. **L2**

Differentiated Instruction: English Learners
Have students make a poster displaying the evolution of the model of the atom. **L2**

Discuss
Discuss how the atomic orbital concept became an accepted model. **L2**

Use Visuals: Table 5.1
Have students look at Table 5.1. Ask several questions that prepare students to understand how many orbitals are probably in level 7. **L2**

Targeted Resources

❏ GRSW: Section 5.1
❏ Transparency: 5.1 Connecting to Your World

3 ASSESS

Evaluate Understanding
Have students distinguish between the valid parts of the Bohr model and those no longer accurate. Ask them to describe the relationships between energy levels, sublevels, orbitals, and electrons. **L2**

Reteach
Review the mathematical relationships relative to electron location. **L1**

Targeted Resources

❏ Interactive Textbook with ChemASAP: Section 5.1

5.2 Electron Arrangement in Atoms

2 Periods, 1 Block

Objectives

5.2.1 Describe how to write the electron configuration for an atom.

5.2.2 Explain why the actual electron configurations for some elements differ from those predicted by the aufbau principle.

Vocabulary

electron configurations • aufbau principle
• Pauli exclusion principle • Hund's rule

Ability Levels

L1 *Basic to Average*
L2 *For All Students*
L3 *Average to Advanced*

National Science Education Standards

A-1, B-1

---

1 FOCUS

Build Vocabulary

Explain how the Latin *configuare* is related to the definition of *electron configuration*. **L2**

---

2 INSTRUCT

Connecting to Your World
Discuss

Develop the electron configurations for several elements, applying the aufbau principle, the Pauli exclusion principle, and Hund's rule as needed. **L2**

Class Activity: Writing Electron Configurations

Have students develop electron configurations for the third period elements. **L2**

Differentiated Instruction: Gifted and Talented

Have students name and explain the second, third, and fourth quantum numbers for an electron orbital. **L3**

Discuss

Explain the effect that the quantum property spin has on an orbital. **L2**

Differentiated Instruction: Special Needs

Have students create cards, one of the aufbau diagram and several with a name and atomic number of an element on one side and its electron configuration on the other side. **L1**

Targeted Resources

❑ Small-Scale Chemistry Lab Manual: Lab 7
❑ GRSW: Section 5.2
❑ Transparency: 5.2 Connecting to Your World
❑ Transparency 59: Aufbau Diagram
❑ Transparency: Conceptual Problem 5.1: Writing Electron Configurations
❑ Go Online: Section 5.2

---

3 ASSESS

Evaluate Understanding

Present students with the symbol and atomic number of various elements throughout the periodic table. Have them provide the electron configuration. **L2**

Reteach

Have small groups of students practice writing electron configurations. **L1**

Targeted Resources

❑ Interactive Textbook with ChemASAP: Section 5.2

5.3 Physics and the Quantum Mechanical Model

4 Periods, 2 Blocks

Objectives

5.3.1 Describe the relationship between the wavelength and frequency of light.

5.3.2 Identify the source of atomic emission spectra.

5.3.3 Explain how the frequencies of light are related to changes in electron energies.

5.3.4 Distinguish between quantum mechanics and classical mechanics.

Vocabulary

amplitude • wavelength • frequency • hertz
• electromagnetic radiation • spectrum
• atomic emission spectrum • ground state
• photons • Heisenberg uncertainty principle

Ability Levels
L1 *Basic to Average*
L2 *For All Students*
L3 *Average to Advanced*

National Science Education Standards

A-1, A-2, B-2, B-6, G-1, G-2, G-3

1 FOCUS

Build Vocabulary

Explain the parts of the word *atomic emission spectrum* that come from Latin. Ask students to figure out what the word *emissary* means. **L2**

2 INSTRUCT

Connecting to Your World
Class Activity: Black Box Discovery

Have students try to determine what objects are inside sealed boxes. **L1**

Use Visuals: Figures 5.12 and 5.13

Ask students to describe the difference between the spectrum of light from a light bulb and the spectrum from a helium lamp. **L1**

Differentiated Instruction: Gifted and Talented

Have students design a system for refracting light and creating a rainbow. **L3**

Relate

Explain how the wave–particle behavior of light explained a previously mysterious photoelectric effect. **L2**

Quick Lab: *Flame Tests* **L2**

Targeted Resources

❑ Laboratory Manual: Labs 6, 7, 8
❑ Small-Scale Chemistry Lab Manual: Lab 8
❑ Laboratory Practical: 5-1, 5-2
❑ GRSW: Section 5.3
❑ Transparency: 5.3 Connecting to Your World
❑ Go Online: Section 5.3

3 ASSESS

Evaluate Understanding

Have students create wave diagrams showing the relationship between wavelength and frequency. Ask them to explain the origin of the groups of lines in the hydrogen spectrum. **L2**

Reteach

Have students explain the significance of each of the illustrations in this section. **L1**

Targeted Resources

❑ Interactive Textbook with ChemASAP: Section 5.3

6.1 Organizing the Elements

2 Periods, 1 Block

Objectives
6.1.1 Explain how elements are organized in a periodic table.
6.1.2 Compare early and modern periodic tables.
6.1.3 Identify three broad classes of elements.

Vocabulary
periodic law • metals • nonmetals • metalloid

Ability Levels
L1 *Basic to Average*
L2 *For All Students*
L3 *Average to Advanced*

National Science Education Standards
A-2, B-2, G-1, G-2, G-3

---

1 FOCUS

Build Vocabulary
Discuss the similarities and differences of the words *metal, metalloid,* and *nonmetal.* **L2**

---

2 INSTRUCT

Connecting to Your World
Teacher Demo: Organizing Elements
Organize samples (or visuals) of pure elements and their properties for students to view. Encourage students to find similarities among elements within a group. **L2**

Use Visuals: Figure 6.3
Have students study Mendeleev's periodic table. Then point out the similarities within rows and the gaps left for elements not yet discovered. **L1**

Use Visuals: Figure 6.5
Ask students what the three numbers at the top of each column in Figure 6.5 represent. Then ask which group has the most elements. **L1**

Differentiated Instruction: Less Proficient Readers
As students read this section, have them add details about each element group to a chart on the board. **L1**

Class Activity: Name the Element
Have each student describe an element trying to get the class to identify it. **L2**

Discuss
Use silicon as an example for discussing metalloids. Explain the relationship between temperature and electrical conductivity for a semiconducting element. **L2**

Targeted Resources
❑ GRSW: Section 6.1
❑ Transparency: 6.1 Connecting to Your World
❑ Transparency 66: Metals, Nonmetals, and Metalloids
❑ Go Online: Section 6.1

---

3 ASSESS

Evaluate Understanding
Have students draw a concept map relating words from this section. **L2**

Reteach
Challenge students to find organizational similarities between a monthly calendar and the periodic table in Figure 6.5. **L1**

Targeted Resources
❑ Interactive Textbook with ChemASAP: Section 6.1

6.2 Classifying the Elements

⏰ *2 Periods, 1 Block*

Objectives

6.2.1 Describe the information in a periodic table.

6.2.2 Classify elements based on electron configuration.

6.2.3 Distinguish representative elements and transition metals.

Vocabulary

alkali metals • alkaline earth metals • halogens • noble gases • representative elements • transition metal • inner transition metal

Ability Levels

L1 *Basic to Average*
L2 *For All Students*
L3 *Average to Advanced*

National Science Education Standards

A-1, B-2, G-2

---

1 FOCUS

Build Vocabulary

Have students use the LINCS strategy to learn the section terms. **L2**

---

2 INSTRUCT

Connecting to Your World
Use Visuals: Figure 6.8

Remind students how to find atomic mass. Review the energy levels of electrons. **L1**

Relate

Have students list all elements that are essential for metabolism in the body. **L2**

Differentiated Instruction: Less Proficient Readers

Have groups of students write electron configurations for a portion of the periodic table. **L1**

Teacher Demo: Observing Differences in Metals

Add HCl to magnesium, tin, and copper to show differences in reactivity. **L2**

Class Activity: Lanthanides in Consumer Products

Ask students to compile a list of consumer products that contain lanthanides or require them for processing. **L2**

Targeted Resources

❏ Laboratory Manual: Lab 9
❏ Laboratory Practical: 6-1, 6-2
❏ GRSW: Section 6.2
❏ Transparency: 6.2 Connecting to Your World
❏ Transparency 68: Periodic Table of the Elements
❏ Transparency 69: Blocks of Elements
❏ Go Online: Section 6.2

---

3 ASSESS

Evaluate Understanding

Have students write electron configurations for elements. Encourage them to increase the speed of writing these. **L2**

Reteach

Reinforce the relationship between configurations and position on the periodic table. **L1**

Targeted Resources

❏ Interactive Textbook with ChemASAP: Section 6.2

6.3 Periodic Trends

2 Periods, 1 Block

Objectives

6.3.1 Describe trends among elements for atomic size.

6.3.2 Explain how ions form.

6.3.3 Describe periodic trends for properties of ions.

Vocabulary

atomic radius • ion • cation • anion • ionization energy • electronegativity

Ability Levels

L1 Basic to Average
L2 For All Students
L3 Average to Advanced

National Science Education Standards

A-2, B-1, B-2, B-3

---

1 FOCUS

Build Vocabulary

Name some representative elements and ask whether they form a cation or anion. **L2**

---

2 INSTRUCT

Connecting to Your World
Use Visuals: Figure 6.13

Point out that the radii in Figure 6.13 are approximations. Ask why it isn't possible to just measure the diameter of a single atom. **L1**

Discuss

Ask students to compare patterns in event seating and prices to positions and properties on the periodic table. **L2**

Class Activity: Listing Elements

Ask students to locate select elements on the periodic table and decide if their atoms will form positive or negative ions. **L2**

Class Activity: Effective Nuclear Charge and Electron Shielding

Using students as models of protons and electrons, show a lithium "nucleus" in order to clarify the concepts of effective nuclear charge and electron shielding. **L2**

Differentiated Instruction: Gifted and Talented

Have students research and describe the phenomenon of the lanthanide contraction. **L3**

Quick Lab: *Periodic Trends in Ionic Radii* **L2**

Targeted Resources

❏ Small-Scale Chemistry Lab Manual: Lab 9
❏ GRSW: Section 6.3
❏ Transparency: 6.3 Connecting to Your World
❏ Transparency 71: Interpreting Graphs: Atomic Radius Versus Atomic Number
❏ Transparency 72: Forming and Sizes of Ions
❏ Transparency 74: Summary of Trends in Groups and Periods
❏ Go Online: Section 6.3

---

3 ASSESS

Evaluate Understanding

Have students compare two elements in the same group in terms of atomic radius, ionic radius, ionization energy, and electronegativity. **L2**

Reteach

Discuss the meanings of the terms in Figure 6.22. Have students practice identifying elements based on a given verbal description of an item's properties. **L1**

Targeted Resources

❏ Interactive Textbook with ChemASAP: Section 6.3

7.1 Ions

 2 Periods, 1 Block

Objectives

7.1.1 Determine the number of valence electrons in an atom of a representative element.

7.1.2 List the elements whose atoms tend to gain electrons and those that tend to lose electrons.

7.1.3 Describe how cations form.

7.1.4 Explain how anions form.

Vocabulary

valence electrons • electron dot structures • octet rule • halide ions

Ability Levels
L1 *Basic to Average*
L2 *For All Students*
L3 *Average to Advanced*

National Science Education Standards

A-1, B-1, B-2

1 FOCUS

Build Vocabulary

Have each student draw a graphic organizer relating a chosen halide ion to the other three vocabulary terms. **L2**

2 INSTRUCT

Connecting to Your World
Discuss

Prompt a conversation about exceptions to the octet rule. **L2**

Teacher Demo: Valence Electrons

Use a plastic egg and marbles to show students how valence electrons can be pulled away more easily than inner electrons. **L2**

Differentiated Instruction: Gifted and Talented

Have students show how the atoms of transition elements become stable with pseudo-noble-gas configurations. **L3**

Class Activity: Forming Cations

Ask students to model the formation of metal cations from metal atoms. **L2**

Differentiated Instruction: Special Needs

Have students work in pairs to practice drawing electron dot structures for Group A elements. **L1**

Use Visuals: Figure 7.5

Point out that arsenic and tellurium are metalloids, yet they form anions that are named like nonmetals. **L1**

Targeted Resources

❏ Small-Scale Chemistry Lab Manual: Lab 10
❏ GRSW: Section 7.1
❏ Transparency: 7.1 Connecting to Your World
❏ Transparency 76: Electron Dot Structure of Some Group A Elements
❏ Transparency 77: Cations of Group 1A and 2A
❏ Transparency 78: Anions of Group 5A, 6A, 7A

3 ASSESS

Evaluate Understanding

Give students a list of ions and have them look at a periodic table to determine whether they are likely to exist. **L2**

Reteach

Randomly select groups from the periodic table and ask students to predict the common ions that could be formed from the elements. **L1**

Targeted Resources

❏ Interactive Textbook with ChemASAP: Section 7.1

7.2 Ionic Bonds and Ionic Compounds

🕐 *2 Periods, 1 Block*

Objectives
7.2.1 Explain the electrical charge of an ionic compound.
7.2.2 Describe three properties of ionic compounds.

Vocabulary
ionic compounds • alkaline earth metals • halogens • ionic bonds • chemical formula • formula unit • coordination number

Ability Levels
L1 *Basic to Average*
L2 *For All Students*
L3 *Average to Advanced*

National Science Education Standards
A-1, B-2, B-3

---

1 FOCUS

Build Vocabulary
Have students skim through the section locating vocabulary terms. Then ask them to paraphrase each definition. **L2**

---

2 INSTRUCT

Connecting to Your World
Discuss
Explain how the formation of positive ions and negative ions are simultaneous and interdependent processes. **L2**

Differentiated Instruction: English Learners
Encourage students to look up and define terms used to describe ionic compounds. They should write definitions in both English and their native language. **L1**

Class Activity: "Hardness" of Water
Have students test water samples for hardness. They will detect the presence of ions. **L2**

Teacher Demo: Form and Structure of Crystals
Pass around crystals of ionic compounds of various types. **L2**

Differentiated Instruction: Gifted and Talented
Have students write the formulas for ionic compounds formed from randomly chosen pairs of cations and anions. **L3**

Quick Lab: *Solutions Containing Ions* **L2**

Targeted Resources
❑ Laboratory Manual: Lab 10
❑ Small-Scale Chemistry Lab Manual: Lab 10
❑ Probeware Lab Manual: Solutions Containing Ions
❑ Laboratory Practical: 7-1
❑ GRSW: Section 7.2
❑ Transparency: 7.2 Connecting to Your World
❑ Transparency 80: Crystalline Structure
❑ Transparency 81: Molten Sodium Chloride
❑ Go Online: Section 7.2

---

3 ASSESS

Evaluate Understanding
Name ionic compounds and ask students to identify the cation, anion, and ration of cations to anions in each. **L2**

Reteach
Review the properties of ionic compounds. Emphasize that they are a collection of independent ions. **L1**

Targeted Resources
❑ Interactive Textbook with ChemASAP: Section 7.2

7.3 Bonding in Metals

⌚ *2 Periods, 1 Block*

Objectives

7.3.1 Model the valence electrons of metal
atoms.
7.3.2 Describe the arrangement of atoms in a
metal.
7.3.3 Explain the importance of alloys.

Vocabulary
metallic bonds • alloys

Ability Levels
L1 *Basic to Average*
L2 *For All Students*
L3 *Average to Advanced*

National Science Education Standards
B-2, B-6

1 FOCUS

Build Vocabulary
Have students infer the meaning of *metallic bond*
based on their knowledge of each word making
up the compound. **L2**

2 INSTRUCT

Connecting to Your World
Relate
Assess students' prior knowledge about metals
by asking them to describe the properties of
malleable and ductile metals. Then ask why it is
unwise to stand in a lightning storm holding a
metal rod. **L2**

Teacher Demo: Copper in a Metal or a Compound
Smash samples of a copper metal and a copper
compound to compare properties. **L2**

Use Visuals: Figure 7.14
Lead a class discussion on the concept of "closest
packing" of metal cations in pure metals. Use the
three arrangements shown in Figure 7.14. **L1**

Differentiated Instruction: Gifted and Talented
Have students develop formulas for calculating
the density of a metal given the atomic radius of
the metal and the cubic unit cell packing
arrangement of the metal atoms. **L3**

Teacher Demo: Types of Alloys
Use toothpicks and foam balls of various sizes
and colors to compare the crystal structures of
interstitial and substitutional alloys. **L2**

Targeted Resources
❑ Laboratory Manual: Lab 10
❑ Laboratory Practical: 7-1
❑ GRSW: Section 7.3
❑ Transparency: 7.3 Connecting to Your World
❑ Transparency 83: Metal Rod Forced Through
   Die
❑ Transparency 84: Metallic Crystal Packing

3 ASSESS

Evaluate Understanding
Ask what the basic model of metal bonding is
and how does this model explain the electrical
conductivity of metals. **L2**

Reteach
Compare and contrast chemical bonding in ionic
compounds and pure metals. **L1**

Targeted Resources
❑ Interactive Textbook with ChemASAP:
   Section 7.3

8.1 Molecular Compounds

2 Periods, 1 Block

Objectives

8.1.1 Distinguish molecular compounds from ionic compounds.

8.1.2 Identify the information a molecular formula provides.

Vocabulary

covalent bond • molecule • diatomic molecule • molecular compound • molecular formula

Ability Levels

L1 *Basic to Average*
L2 *For All Students*
L3 *Average to Advanced*

National Science Education Standards

B-2

1 FOCUS

Build Vocabulary

Explain the meaning of the word *covalent*, and have students name other words beginning with the prefix *co-*. **L2**

2 INSTRUCT

Connecting to Your World
Use Visuals: Figure 8.1

Point out that although helium, neon, and other noble gases exist as monatomic gases, some other elements are most stable when two atoms are joined together. **L1**

Teacher Demo: Molecular Structures and Formulas

Construct models of several pairs of molecules. Show students each pair and ask them how many of each type of atom is in each molecule. **L2**

Relate

Describe many of the large, complex molecules found in nature that are molecular compounds. **L1**

Differentiated Instruction: English Learners

Prepare large, 3-dimensional models of ammonia similar to the two in Figure 8.5 and cards with structural formulas. Hold up the models and point out the information that each model or formula provides. **L1**

Targeted Resources

❏ GRSW: Section 8.1
❏ Transparency: 8.1 Connecting to Your World
❏ Transparency 86: Ammonia Molecule
❏ Go Online: Section 8.1

3 ASSESS

Evaluate Understanding

Have students label a series of statements as true or false. **L2**

Reteach

Write a series of formulas on the board. Ask students to identify any substance that does not exist. **L1**

Targeted Resources

❏ Interactive Textbook with ChemASAP: Section 8.1

8.2 The Nature of Covalent Bonding

6 Periods, 3 Blocks

Objectives

8.2.1 State a rule that usually tells you how many electrons are shared to form covalent bonds.

8.2.2 Demonstrate how electron dot diagrams are used.

8.2.3 Apply a rule to determine when two atoms are likely to be joined by a double or triple bond.

8.2.4 Distinguish between a covalent bond and a coordinate covalent bond.

8.2.5 Describe how the strength of a covalent bond is related to its bond dissociation energy.

8.2.6 Identify exceptions to the octet rule.

Ability Levels

L1 *Basic to Average*
L2 *For All Students*
L3 *Average to Advanced*

National Science Education Standards

A-1, A-2, B-2, G-2

Vocabulary

single covalent bond • structural formula • unshared pair • double covalent bond • triple covalent bond • coordinate covalent bond • polyatomic ion • bond dissociation energy • resonance structure

1 FOCUS

Build Vocabulary

Explain the meaning of the word *structure* and ask students to define *structural steel*. **L2**

2 INSTRUCT

Connecting to Your World
Differentiated Instruction: Special Needs

Pair each student with a study partner. Have them use the periodic table and quiz each other on writing electron structures for single atoms and for bonded atoms. **L1**

Class Activity: Bonding for Second Row Elements

Have students draw electron dot formulas for each element in the second row of the periodic table. **L2**

Relate

Discuss the role and nature of nitrogen with students. **L1**

Teacher Demo: Bond Energies

Use a Bunsen burner to show students two reactions in which bonds are formed. Compare ionic and covalent bond energies. **L2**

Quick Lab: *Strengths of Covalent Bonds* **L2**

Targeted Resources

❏ Probeware Lab Manual: Strengths of Covalent Bonds

❏ GRSW: Section 8.2

❏ Transparency: 8.2 Connecting to Your World

❏ Transparency: Conceptual Problem 8.1: Drawing an Electron Dot Formula

❏ Go Online: Section 8.2

3 ASSESS

Evaluate Understanding

Ask students to write electrons structures for several compounds. Have pairs of students decide whether their structures are correct and work together to correct any errors. **L2**

Targeted Resources

❏ Interactive Textbook with ChemASAP: Section 8.2

8.3 Bonding Theories

🕐 *2 Periods, 1 Block*

Objectives

8.3.1 Describe the relationship between atomic and molecular orbitals.

8.3.2 Describe how VSEPR theory helps predict the shapes of molecules.

8.3.3 Identify ways in which orbital hybridization is useful in describing molecules.

Vocabulary

molecular orbitals • bonding orbital • sigma bond • pi bond • tetrahedral angle • VSEPR theory • hybridization

Ability Levels
- **L1** *Basic to Average*
- **L2** *For All Students*
- **L3** *Average to Advanced*

National Science Education Standards

B-2, E-2

1 FOCUS

Build Vocabulary

The hybridization of atomic orbitals is the combining of two or more orbitals to form a single orbital that is different from those that were combined. **L2**

2 INSTRUCT

Connecting to Your World
Using Visuals: Figure 8.13

Have students note the positions of the two nuclei in the two hydrogen atomic orbitals. **L2**

Discuss

Describe a visualization of the formation of the covalent bond in H_2. **L2**

Relate

Compare the methods of topographic maps with the way scientists use electron densities. **L2**

Differentiated Instruction: Gifted and Talented

Gifted students may want to access a college text and learn more about molecular orbital theory and how it explains the paradox of bonding in the oxygen molecule. **L3**

Class Activity: Making Molecular Models

Students will achieve an understanding of simple molecular shapes and relate the actual three-dimensional geometry to two-dimensional illustrations. **L2**

Targeted Resources

- ❑ Laboratory Manual: Lab 11
- ❑ Small-Scale Chemistry Lab Manual: Lab 11
- ❑ Laboratory Practical: 8-1, 8-2
- ❑ GRSW: Section 8.3
- ❑ Transparency: 8.3 Connecting to Your World
- ❑ Transparency 91: Sigma and pi Orbitals
- ❑ Transparency 92: Tetrahedral Molecule Structure
- ❑ Go Online: Section 8.3

3 ASSESS

Evaluate Understanding

Have students compare and contrast the characteristics of sigma and pi bonds. **L2**

Reteach

Divide students into pairs to determine the shapes of molecules by means of the VSEPR theory. **L1**

Targeted Resources

- ❑ Interactive Textbook with ChemASAP: Section 8.3

8.4 Polar Bonds and Molecules

4 Periods, 2 Blocks

Objectives

8.4.1 Describe how electronegativity values determine the distribution of charge in a polar molecule.

8.4.2 Describe what happens to polar molecules when they are placed between oppositely charged metal plates.

8.4.3 Evaluate the strength of intermolecular attractions compared with the strength of ionic and covalent bonds.

8.4.4 Identify the reason why network solids have high melting points or decompose before melting.

Ability Levels

L1 *Basic to Average*
L2 *For All Students*
L3 *Average to Advanced*

National Science Education Standards

A-1, B-2

Vocabulary

nonpolar covalent bond • polar covalent bond • polar bond • polar molecule • dipole • van der Waals forces • dipole interactions • dispersion forces • hydrogen bonds • network solids

1 FOCUS

Build Vocabulary

Explain the meaning of the Latin stem *polus* and how it relates to the words *polar, nonpolar,* and *dipole.* **L2**

2 INSTRUCT

Connecting to Your World
Discuss

Ask students what the term *electronegativity* means. Ask them which element is the most and least electronegative. **L1**

Class Activity: A Magnetic Analogy

Students will experience the attraction of opposite poles of a magnet as an experience similar to the attraction of opposite electric charges. **L2**

Teacher Demo: Observing Evidence of Polarity

Students will observe evidence that polar molecules show electrostatic attractions to charged molecules. **L2**

Discuss

Construct a concept map using the following terms: *intermolecular attractions, van der Waals forces, dispersion forces, dipole interactions,* and *hydrogen bonding.* **L2**

Targeted Resources

❑ GRSW: Section 8.4
❑ Transparency: 8.4 Connecting to Your World
❑ Go Online: Section 8.4

3 ASSESS

Evaluate Understanding

Have students account for the generally low melting points of covalent compounds in terms of bonding. **L2**

Reteach

Help students list the types of intermolecular attractions that operate between molecules. **L1**

Targeted Resources

❑ Interactive Textbook with ChemASAP: Section 8.4

9.1 Naming Ions

2 Periods, 1 Block

Objectives

9.1.1 Determine the charges of monatomic ions by using the periodic table and **write** the names of the ions.

9.1.2 Determine a polyatomic ion and **write** the names and formulas of the most common polyatomic ions.

9.1.3 Identify the two common endings for the names of most polyatomic ions.

Vocabulary

monatomic ion • polyatomic ion

Ability Levels

L1 *Basic to Average*
L2 *For All Students*
L3 *Average to Advanced*

National Science Education Standards

A-1, A-2, B-2, G-1

1 FOCUS

Build Vocabulary

Have students to list words that begin with the prefixes *mono-* and *poly-*. Then, ask students how they think monatomic ions and polyatomic ions might differ. **L2**

2 INSTRUCT

Connecting to Your World
Teacher Demo: Colorful Ions

Show students beakers containing solutions of soluble metal salts. Have students describe the colors of the solutions and practice naming the ions. **L2**

Relate

Divide students into research teams to gather data about paint pigments. **L2**

Differentiated Instruction: Special Needs

Give students different-colored disks to represent protons and electrons in neutral atoms. Remove or add electrons and ask students to find the charge of the resulting "ion." **L1**

Use Visuals: Table 9.3

Have students pick out the *-ate/-ite* pairs of ions in Table 9.3 and write their formulas. **L1**

Class Activity: Shapes of Polyatomic Ions

Students prepare ball-and-stick models of polyatomic ions. **L2**

Targeted Resources

❑ GRSW: Section 9.1
❑ Transparency: 9.1 Connecting to Your World
❑ Transparency: Conceptual Problem 9.1: Classifying and Naming Cations and Anions
❑ Go Online: Section 9.1

3 ASSESS

Evaluate Understanding

Have students evaluate chemical symbols of atoms or groups of atoms. Ask which can exist as ions and which cannot be transformed into ions. **L2**

Reteach

Explain that polyatomic ions are not found free in nature. Remind students that polyatomic ions carry a charge, so they are found combined with other ions in compounds. **L1**

Targeted Resources

❑ Interactive Textbook with ChemASAP: Section 9.1

9.2 Naming and Writing Formulas for Ionic Compounds

2 Periods, 1 Block

Objectives
9.2.1 Apply the rules for naming and writing formulas for binary ionic compounds.

9.2.2 Apply the rules for naming and writing formulas for compounds with polyatomic ions.

Vocabulary
binary compound

Ability Levels
L1 *Basic to Average*
L2 *For All Students*
L3 *Average to Advanced*

National Science Education Standards
A-1, B-2, G-2, G-3

1 FOCUS

Build Vocabulary
Explain that the word *compound* comes from the Latin word *componere*, which means "to put." **L2**

2 INSTRUCT

Connecting to Your World
Class Activity: Naming Ionic Binary Compounds
Teams of students examine formulas to practice naming binary compounds. **L2**

Differentiated Instruction: Less Proficient Readers
Have students use index cards to compose formulas for ionic compounds. **L1**

Teacher Demo: Making and Naming an Ionic Compound
Show students a reaction in which an ionic compound is formed. Have students name the compound and write its formula. **L2**

Use Visuals: Figure 9.10
Have students name the formulas for the ionic compounds mentioned in the caption of Figure 9.10. **L2**

Differentiated Instruction: Gifted and Talented
Have interested students research the possible mechanisms for the alleviation of symptoms of bipolar disorder by lithium ions. **L3**

Targeted Resources
❑ Small-Scale Chemistry Lab Manual: Lab 12
❑ GRSW: Section 9.2
❑ Transparency: 9.2 Connecting to Your World
❑ Transparency: Conceptual Problem 9.2: Writing Formulas for Binary Ionic Compounds
❑ Go Online: Section 9.2

3 ASSESS

Evaluate Understanding
Write cations and anions on the board. Have students name and write formula units for all possible ionic compounds that the ions could form. **L2**

Reteach
Review the procedures for naming ionic compounds, binary compounds, and compounds with polyatomic ions. **L1**

Targeted Resources
❑ Interactive Textbook with ChemASAP: Section 9.2

9.3 Naming and Writing Formulas for Molecular Compounds

2 Periods, 1 Block

Objectives

9.3.1 Interpret the prefixes in the names of molecular compounds in terms of their chemical formulas.

9.3.2 Apply the rules for naming and writing formulas for binary molecular compounds.

Ability Levels

L1 *Basic to Average*
L2 *For All Students*
L3 *Average to Advanced*

National Science Education Standards

B-2

1 FOCUS

Build Vocabulary

Tell students that prefixes such as *di-*, *tri-*, and *tetra-* indicate how many atoms of each element are in a molecular compound. **L2**

2 INSTRUCT

Connecting to Your World
Class Activity: Naming Binary Molecular Compounds

Students name formulas by converting subscripts in the formulas to prefixes in the names. **L2**

Discuss

Explain how the order of the elements in the names of most molecular compounds is established. **L2**

Differentiated Instruction: Gifted and Talented

Have students research global warming. Students can prepare oral, written, or visual presentations. **L3**

Targeted Resources

❏ GRSW: Section 9.3
❏ Transparency: 9.3 Connecting to Your World
❏ Go Online: Section 9.3

3 ASSESS

Evaluate Understanding

Have students write formulas and names for several molecular compounds. Then, challenge students to name pairs of compounds and identify what each pair has in common. **L2**

Reteach

Have students write the names for binary molecular formulas and the formulas for compound names. **L1**

Targeted Resources

❏ Interactive Textbook with ChemASAP: Section 9.3

9.4 Naming and Writing Formulas for Acids and Bases

⏱ *1 Period, ¹/₂ Block*

Objectives

9.4.1 Apply three rules for naming acids.

9.4.2 Apply the rules in reverse to write formulas of acids.

9.4.3 Apply the rules for naming bases.

Vocabulary

acid • base

Ability Levels

L1 *Basic to Average*
L2 *For All Students*
L3 *Average to Advanced*

National Science Education Standards

A-1, B-2

1 FOCUS

Build Vocabulary

Ask students if the words *acid* or *acidic* are applied to any foods they eat. **L2**

2 INSTRUCT

Connecting to Your World
Use Visuals: Figure 9.14

Have students compare the vulnerability of glass and the vulnerability of wax to reaction with hydrofluoric acid. **L2**

Use Visuals: Table 9.5

Ask students questions about naming anions switch the endings *-ide, -ite,* and *-ate.* Encourage students to use Table 9.5 until they are comfortable with naming acids. **L2**

Discuss

Discuss the ending *-ic* in the acid name *perchloric acid.* Have students name the anion, give the formula, and tell how many hydrogen atoms will combine with the perchlorate ion. **L2**

Relate

Describe the power of strong bases such as sodium hydroxide. **L1**

Targeted Resources

❑ GRSW: Section 9.4
❑ Transparency: 9.4 Connecting to Your World
❑ Go Online: Section 9.4

3 ASSESS

Evaluate Understanding

Assign groups of students a number of the polyatomic ions listed in Table 9.3. Have them write the formulas for the corresponding acids and name the acids. **L2**

Reteach

Using Table 9.5 as a model, have students name anions and write their formulas. **L1**

Targeted Resources

❑ Interactive Textbook with ChemASAP: Section 9.4

9.5 The Laws Governing Formulas and Names

2 Periods, 1 Block

Objectives

9.5.1 Define the laws of definition proportions and multiple proportions.

9.5.2 Apply the rules for writing chemical formulas by using a flowchart.

9.5.3 Apply the rules for naming chemical compounds by using a flowchart.

Vocabulary

law of definite proportions • law of multiple proportions

Ability Levels
L1 *Basic to Average*
L2 *For All Students*
L3 *Average to Advanced*

National Science Education Standards
A-1, B-2

1 FOCUS

Build Vocabulary

Define *scientific law*. Explain the two laws that govern the formation of chemical compounds, the law of definite proportions and the law of multiple proportions. **L2**

2 INSTRUCT

Connecting to Your World
Use Visuals: Figure 9.16

Ask students to use the models shown in Figure 9.16 to determine the formulas for the two compounds. Have students identify other ways to tell the two compounds apart. **L1**

Discuss

Ask students what they can determine about CO and CO_2 based on the laws of definite proportions and multiple proportions. **L2**

Relate

Have students think of other situations where specific names are important for accurate or fast results. **L2**

Differentiated Instruction: Special Needs

Pair students who have difficulty with mathematics with students with strong math skills to get help with the laws of definite proporations and multiple proportions. **L1**

Quick Lab: *Making Ionic Compounds* **L2**

Targeted Resources

❏ Laboratory Practical: 9-1
❏ GRSW: Section 9.5
❏ Transparency: 9.5 Connecting to Your World
❏ Transparency: Sample Problem 9.1: Calculating Mass Ratios
❏ Transparency 103: Writing Chemical Formulas

3 ASSESS

Evaluate Understanding

Have students use Figure 9.20 to name compounds when given the formulas. Have students use Figure 9.22 to write formulas when given the names of compounds. **L2**

Reteach

Review the four guidelines for writing chemical formulas. Give students the names of compounds, and have them use Figure 9.22 to determine the corresponding formulas. **L1**

Targeted Resources

❏ Interactive Textbook with ChemASAP: Section 9.5

10.1 The Mole: A Measurement of Matter

2 Periods, 1 Block

Objectives

10.1.1 Describe methods of measuring the amount of something.

10.1.2 Relate Avogadro's number to a mole of a substance.

10.1.3 Compare and contrast the atomic mass of an element and its molar mass.

10.1.4 Calculate the mass of a mole of a compound.

Vocabulary

mole (mol) • Avogadro's number
• representative particle • molar mass

Ability Levels

L1 *Basic to Average*
L2 *For All Students*
L3 *Average to Advanced*

National Science Education Standards

A-1, A-2, B-1, B-2

1 FOCUS

Build Vocabulary

Have students write two or three sentences relating *mole* to the other vocabulary words. **L2**

2 INSTRUCT

Connecting to Your World
Relate

Point out several conversion factors that students use on a regular basis. **L1**

Differentiated Instruction: English Learners

Team students who are proficient in English with students who have strong math skills. **L1**

Use Visuals: Figure 10.3

Have students study Figure 10.3 and read the text that discusses the number of particles in a mole. **L1**

Relate

Write several numbers on the board using standard notation. Have students rewrite the numbers using scientific notation. **L2**

Discuss

Point out to students that the mass of a single atom can be expressed in atomic mass units, but it is not realistic to work with single atoms. **L2**

Targeted Resources

❏ Small-Scale Chemistry Lab Manual: Lab 13
❏ GRSW: Section 10.1
❏ Transparency: 10.1 Connecting to Your World
❏ Transparency: Sample Problem 10.1: Finding Mass from a Count
❏ Transparency 106: Molar Mass
❏ Transparency: Sample Problem 10.4: Finding the Molar Mass of a Compound
❏ Go Online: Section 10.1

3 ASSESS

Evaluate Understanding

Ask students questions concerning the quantity of a mole. **L2**

Reteach

Set up cooperative learning groups of three or four students to answer problems and perform calculations. **L1**

Targeted Resources

❏ Interactive Textbook with ChemASAP: Section 10.1

10.2 Mole–Mass and Mole–Volume Relationships

2 Periods, 1 Block

Objectives

10.2.1 Convert the mass of a substance to the number of moles of a substance, and moles to mass.

10.2.2 Calculate the volume of a quantity of gas at STP.

Vocabulary

Avogadro's hypothesis • standard temperature and pressure (STP) • molar volume

Ability Levels

L1 *Basic to Average*
L2 *For All Students*
L3 *Average to Advanced*

National Science Education Standards

A-1, A-2, B-2

1 FOCUS

Build Vocabulary

Have students make notes in three columns to show what they know, what they want to know, and what they learn as they read the section. **L2**

2 INSTRUCT

Connecting to Your World
Discuss

Review the mathematical conversions of grams to moles and moles to grams. **L2**

Relate

Use knowledge of moles to determine the relationship between reactants and products. **L2**

Differentiated Instruction: Less Proficient Readers

Have students analyze problems for the information contained. Students should look for key words. **L1**

Discuss

Ask students questions about the mole–volume relationship. **L2**

Use Visuals: Figure 10.12

Guide students through examples of various mole conversions. **L1**

Targeted Resources

❑ Laboratory Manual: Lab 12
❑ GRSW: Section 10.2
❑ Transparency: 10.2 Connecting to Your World
❑ Transparency 109: The Mole Road Map

3 ASSESS

Evaluate Understanding

Have students work problems in which they use molar mass and molar volume to calculate the densities of gases. **L2**

Reteach

Review the concept of density as a ratio of mass to volume. **L1**

Targeted Resources

❑ Interactive Textbook with ChemASAP: Section 10.2

10.3 Percent Composition and Chemical Formulas

🕐 *2 Periods, 1 Block*

Objectives

10.3.1 **Calculate** the percent by mass of an element in a compound.

10.3.2 **Interpret** an empirical formula.

10.3.3 **Compare and contrast** empirical and molecular formulas.

Vocabulary

percent composition • empirical formula

Ability Levels

L1 *Basic to Average*
L2 *For All Students*
L3 *Average to Advanced*

National Science Education Standards

A-1, A-2, B-2

---

1 FOCUS

Build Vocabulary

Have students define *percent composition* in their own words. Then, have them check the definition in the dictionary. **L2**

---

2 INSTRUCT

Connecting to Your World
Differentiated Instruction: Gifted and Talented

Have students research the formulas of the three different oxides of iron. **L3**

Class Activity: Empirical Formulas from Percent Composition

Students use an analogy to clarify the concepts of percent composition and empirical formulas. **L2**

Quick Lab: *Percent Composition* **L2**

Targeted Resources

❏ Laboratory Manual: Lab 13
❏ Laboratory Practical: 10-1, 10-2
❏ GRSW: Section 10.3
❏ Transparency: 10.3 Connecting to Your World
❏ Transparency: Sample Problem 10.9: Calculating the Percent Composition from Mass Data
❏ Transparency: Sample Problem 10.11: Determining the Empirical Formula of a Compound
❏ Go Online: Section 10.3

---

3 ASSESS

Evaluate Understanding

Have students list the steps they would take to calculate the molecular formula in several different situations. **L2**

Reteach

Point out to students that when they know the percent composition and molar mass of a compound, they must first use they percent composition to calculate the empirical formula. They can then do the rest. **L1**

Targeted Resources

❏ Interactive Textbook with ChemASAP: Section 10.3

11.1 Describing Chemical Reactions

2 Periods, 1 Block

Objectives

11.1.1 Explain how to write a word equation.

11.1.2 Describe how to write a skeleton equation.

11.1.3 List the steps for writing a complete chemical equation.

Vocabulary

chemical equation • skeleton equation
• catalyst • coefficients • balanced equation

Ability Levels

L1 *Basic to Average*
L2 *For All Students*
L3 *Average to Advanced*

National Science Education Standards

A-1, A-2, B-3, G-1

1 FOCUS

Build Vocabulary

Write a chemical equation on the board and have students discuss each vocabulary term in reference to the equation. **L2**

2 INSTRUCT

Connecting to Your World
Use Visuals: Figure 11.1

Ask students for some indications that a chemical reaction is taking place. Have students describe some commercial uses for yeast. **L2**

Differentiated Instruction: English Learners

Spanish-speaking students with limited English proficiency may find it helpful to consult the chapter summary and key terms in the Spanish supplement in the Teacher's Resource Package as they read. **L1**

Relate

Initiate a discussion with students about the kinds of reactions that take place in nature. Mention that quite frequently the products of one reaction become the reactants of a subsequent reaction. **L2**

Teacher Demo: An Example of Chemical Change

Students will observe the results of a reaction in which table sugar is dehydrated by concentrated sulfuric acid, leaving a porous, foam cylinder of carbon. **L2**

Quick Lab: *Removing Silver Tarnish* **L2**

Targeted Resources

❏ Small-Scale Chemistry Lab Manual: Lab 14
❏ GRSW: Section 11.1
❏ Transparency: 11.1 Connecting to Your World
❏ Transparency 114: Chemical and Physical Changes
❏ Transparency: Conceptual Problem 11.3: Balancing a Chemical Equation
❏ Go Online: Section 11.1

3 ASSESS

Evaluate Understanding

To evaluate students' understanding of how to write and interpret chemical equations, write some word equations on the board and have students produce skeleton equations, using symbols from Table 11.1. **L2**

Reteach

Review with students the key steps in writing balanced equations. Have them make a flowchart to describe the best way to subdivide the task. **L1**

Targeted Resources

❏ Interactive Textbook with ChemASAP: Section 11.1

11.2 Types of Chemical Reactions

2 Periods, 1 Block

Objectives

11.2.1 Describe the five general types of reactions.

11.2.2 Predict the products of the five general types of reactions.

Vocabulary

combination reaction • decomposition reaction • single-replacement reaction • activity series • double-replacement reaction • combustion reaction

Ability Levels
L1 *Basic to Average*
L2 *For All Students*
L3 *Average to Advanced*

National Science Education Standards
A-1, A-2, B-3

1 FOCUS

Build Vocabulary

Have students draw concept maps entitled "Types of chemical reactions." Have them include all the vocabulary terms in the concept map, as well as descriptions and examples of each type of reaction. **L2**

2 INSTRUCT

Connecting to Your World
Discuss

Write the names of ionic and molecular compounds on the board. Review the names and formulas for common inorganic compounds. **L2**

Differentiated Instruction: Gifted and Talented

Have students research the meaning of *synthesis*. Have them investigate the synthesis of polymers and the process of photosynthesis. **L3**

Teacher Demo: Single-Replacement Reactions

Students will observe single-replacement reactions, as metal replaces hydrogen in two different reactions. **L2**

Relate

Ask students to infer why it is important that combustion reactions take place in properly ventilated areas. **L2**

Targeted Resources

❏ Laboratory Manual: Labs 14, 15
❏ Small-Scale Chemistry Lab Manual: Lab 15
❏ Laboratory Practical: 11-1
❏ GRSW: Section 11.2
❏ Transparency: 11.2 Connecting to Your World
❏ Transparency 119: Combination Reaction, Part 1
❏ Transparency 120: Decomposition Reaction, Part 2
❏ Go Online: Section 11.2

3 ASSESS

Evaluate Understanding

Ask students to give an example of each type of reaction discussed in this section. **L2**

Reteach

Help students develop a branched flowchart similar to those used in qualitative analysis. **L1**

Targeted Resources

❏ Interactive Textbook with ChemASAP: Section 11.2

11.3 Reactions in Aqueous Solution

2 Periods, 1 Block

Objectives

11.3.1 Describe the information found in a net ionic equation.

11.3.2 Predict the formation of a precipitate in a double-replacement reaction.

Vocabulary

complete ionic equation • spectator ion • net ionic equation

Ability Levels

L1 *Basic to Average*
L2 *For All Students*
L3 *Average to Advanced*

National Science Education Standards

A-1, A-2, B-3

1 FOCUS

Build Vocabulary

Have students write a complete ionic equation, and circle the spectator ions. From this result, have them write the net ionic equation for the reaction. **L2**

2 INSTRUCT

Connecting to Your World

Discuss

Ask several questions to assess students' prior knowledge about precipitation reactions. **L2**

Relate

Explain that underground caverns form when carbonic acid dissolves the calcium carbonate in limestone. **L2**

Differentiated Instruction: Less Proficient Readers

Initiate a discussion with students about precipitation reactions that occur in everyday life. **L1**

Targeted Resources

❏ Targeted Resources
❏ Laboratory Manual: Labs 16, 17, 18
❏ Small-Scale Chemistry Lab Manual: Labs 16, 17
❏ Laboratory Practical: 11-2, 11-3, 11-4, 11-5
❏ GRSW: Section 11.3
❏ Transparency: 11.3 Connecting to Your World

3 ASSESS

Evaluate Understanding

To evaluate students' understanding of complete ionic equations, net ionic equations, and the formation of precipitates, write some sentences for precipitation reaction on the board. **L2**

Reteach

Review with students the writing and balancing of complete and net ionic equations and the use of the rules of solubility to predict the outcome of double-replacement reactions. **L1**

Targeted Resources

❏ Interactive Textbook with ChemASAP: Section 11.3

12.1 The Arithmetic of Equations

⏱ *2 Periods, 1 Block*

Objectives

12.1.1 Calculate the amounts of reactants required or product formed in a nonchemical process.

12.1.2 Interpret balanced chemical equations in terms of interacting moles, representative particles, masses, and gas volume at STP.

Vocabulary

stoichiometry

Ability Levels

L1 *Basic to Average*
L2 *For All Students*
L3 *Average to Advanced*

National Science Education Standards

A-1, A-2, B-3

1 FOCUS

Build Vocabulary

Introduce the term *stoichiometry* in your own words. **L2**

2 INSTRUCT

Connecting to Your World
Discuss

Review writing and balancing chemical reactions by writing several unbalanced equations on the board. **L2**

Use Visuals: Figure 12.3

Ask students why the volume of a gas is usually measured at STP. **L1**

Teacher Demo: Interpreting a Chemical Change

Have students observe the reaction caused by adding a strip of magnesium to hydrochloric acid. Then ask them to write a balanced chemical equation of this reaction. **L2**

Differentiated Instruction: Less Proficient Readers

Have students construct a table like the one shown in Figure 12.3 for the reaction of hydrogen gas with oxygen gas to form water. **L1**

Targeted Resources

❏ Laboratory Manual: Lab 19
❏ Laboratory Practical: 12-1
❏ GRSW: Section 12.1
❏ Transparency: 12.1 Connecting to Your World
❏ Transparency: Sample Problem 12.1: Using a Balanced Equation as a Recipe
❏ Transparency 124: Balanced Chemical Equation for Formation of Ammonia
❏ Transparency: Conceptual Problem 12.1: Interpreting a Balanced Chemical Equation
❏ Go Online: Section 12.1

3 ASSESS

Evaluate Understanding

Have paired students write balanced chemical equations and then exchange their equations with other pairs of students to write quantitative relationships between reactants and products. **L2**

Reteach

Remind students that the coefficients in a balanced chemical equation state the relationships among substances involved in the reaction. **L1**

Targeted Resources

❏ Interactive Textbook with ChemASAP: Section 12.1

12.2 Chemical Calculations

2 Periods, 1 Block

Objectives

12.2.1 Construct mole ratios from balanced chemical equations and **apply** these ratios in mole-mole stoichiometric calculations.

12.2.2 Calculate stoichiometric quantities from balanced chemical equations using units of moles, mass, representative particles, and volumes of gases at STP.

Ability Levels
L1 *Basic to Average*
L2 *For All Students*
L3 *Average to Advanced*

National Science Education Standards

A-1, A-2, B-3

1 FOCUS

Build Vocabulary

Have partnered students define *mole ratio* in their own words and share their definitions with the class. **L2**

2 INSTRUCT

Connecting to Your World
Use Visuals: Figure 12.4

Ask students what factors they would need to consider to meet demands for ammonia if they were managing the manufacturing facility in Figure 12.4. **L2**

Differentiated Instruction: Less Proficient Readers

Encourage students to find a method of problem solving that works best for them. To represent reactants and products a visual learner might draw pictures and a kinesthetic learner might manipulate molecular models. **L1**

Discuss

Explain that a mole conversion is a necessary intermediate step in stoichiometric calculations because the number of grams in one mole of a substance varies with its molar mass. **L2**

Class Activity: Stoichiometric Flash Cards

Have students create cards to aid in sequencing the steps for solving stoichiometric problems. **L2**

Targeted Resources

❑ Laboratory Manual: Lab 19
❑ Small-Scale Chemistry Lab Manual: Labs 18, 19
❑ Probeware Lab Manual: Analysis of Baking Soda
❑ Laboratory Practical: 12-2
❑ GRSW: Section 12.2
❑ Transparency: 12.2 Connecting to Your World
❑ Transparency: Sample Problem 12.2: Calculating Moles of a Product
❑ Transparency 129: Stoichiometric Problem Solving
❑ Transparency: Sample Problem 12.6: Finding the Volume of a Gas Needed for a Reaction

3 ASSESS

Evaluate Understanding

Write a balanced equation on the board and have students write all the different mole ratios for the reaction. **L2**

Reteach

Use molecular models to review the importance of mole ratios. **L1**

Targeted Resources

❑ Interactive Textbook with ChemASAP: Section 12.2

12.3 Limiting Reagent and Percent Yield

2 Periods, 1 Block

Objectives

12.3.1 Identify and use the limiting reagent in a reaction to calculate the maximum amount of product(s) produced and the amount of excess reagent.

12.3.2 Calculate theoretical yield, actual yield, or percent yield given appropriate information.

Vocabulary

limiting reagent • excess reagent • theoretical yield • actual yield • percent yield

Ability Levels
L1 *Basic to Average*
L2 *For All Students*
L3 *Average to Advanced*

National Science Education Standards

A-1, A-2, B-3

---

1 FOCUS

Build Vocabulary
Have students use the LINCS strategy for *theoretical yield, actual yield,* and *percent yield.* **L2**

---

2 INSTRUCT

Connecting to Your World
Use Visuals: Figure 12.12
Ask students to name other examples of processes or activities being "limited" on an everyday basis. **L1**

Teacher Demo: Limiting Factor
Using bottles, caps, and containers to hold caps, model the concept of a limiting reagent. **L2**

Differentiated Instruction: Less Proficient Readers
Compare examples of everyday situations to the concept of a limiting reagent. **L1**

Quick Lab: *Limiting Reagents* **L2**

Targeted Resources
❑ Laboratory Manual: Lab 20
❑ GRSW: Section 12.3
❑ Transparency: 12.3 Connecting to Your World
❑ Transparency 134: Equation and Experimental Conditions for Ammonia Synthesis
❑ Transparency: Sample Problem 12.10: Calculating the Percent Yield of a Reaction
❑ Go Online: Section 12.3

---

3 ASSESS

Evaluate Understanding
Place a small piece of zinc in a large beaker of dilute hydrochloric acid and explain the reaction to students. Then ask which of the two reactants is the limiting reagent and how can this hypothesis be tested. **L2**

Reteach
Emphasize the importance of having a correctly balanced equation in order to properly calculate the maximum theoretical yield for a reaction. **L1**

Targeted Resources
❑ Interactive Textbook with ChemASAP: Section 12.3

13.1 The Nature of Gases

2 Periods, 1 Block

Objectives

13.1.1 Describe the three assumptions of the kinetic theory as it applies to gases.

13.1.2 Interpret gas pressure in terms of kinetic theory.

13.1.3 Define the relationship between the Kelvin temperature and the average kinetic energy of particles.

Vocabulary

kinetic energy • kinetic theory • gas pressure • vacuum • atmospheric pressure • barometers • pascal (Pa) • standard atmosphere (atm)

Ability Levels

L1 *Basic to Average*
L2 *For All Students*
L3 *Average to Advanced*

National Science Education Standards

A-1, A-2, B-2, B-5

1 FOCUS

Build Vocabulary

Ask students to explain why a vacuum cleaner is so-named since *vacuum* comes from the Latin word *vacare*, meaning "to be empty." **L2**

2 INSTRUCT

Connecting to Your World
Use Visuals: Figure 13.2

Ask students to look at Figure 13.2 and find the air pressure on top of Mount Everest in terms of kPa. **L1**

Discuss

Hold up an inflated balloon and ask students to describe how the pressure inside the balloon would change if collisions between gas molecules were not perfectly elastic. **L2**

Teacher Demo: Air Pressure

Using an aluminum can, water, foil, and a hot plate, show students the incredible pressure that is exerted by Earth's atmosphere. **L2**

Class Activity: Particle Motion and Pressure

Have students fill containers with various amounts of ball bearings, shake each container, and explain the relationship between the number of gas particles in a container and its pressure. **L2**

Targeted Resources

❑ GRSW: Section 13.1
❑ Transparency: 13.1 Connecting to Your World
❑ Transparency 140: Atmospheric Pressure at Sea Level and on Top of Mt. Everest
❑ Transparency 141: Interpreting Graphs: Distribution of Molecular Kinetic Energy
❑ Go Online: Section 13.1

3 ASSESS

Evaluate Understanding

Ask students what kinetic energy is and how the average kinetic energy of a collection of particles changes with temperature. **L2**

Reteach

Use an air-filled balloon and a small pan of liquid nitrogen to illustrate the effect of temperature on the pressure of a gas. **L1**

Targeted Resources

❑ Interactive Textbook with ChemASAP: Section 13.1

13.2 The Nature of Liquids

2 Periods, 1 Block

Objectives

13.2.1 Identify the factors that determine physical properties of a liquid.

13.2.2 Define evaporation in terms of kinetic energy.

13.2.3 Characterize a system that has a constant vapor pressure.

13.2.4 Identify the conditions under which boiling occurs.

Vocabulary

vaporization • evaporation • vapor pressure • boiling point • normal boiling point

Ability Levels

L1 *Basic to Average*
L2 *For All Students*
L3 *Average to Advanced*

National Science Education Standards

A-2, B-2, B-5

1 FOCUS

Build Vocabulary

Have students make a concept map using the following terms: *vaporization, contained liquid, uncontained liquid, evaporation, condensation, dynamic equilibrium*, and *vapor pressure.* **L2**

2 INSTRUCT

Connecting to Your World
Differentiated Instruction: Special Needs

Have students write a narrative about molecular events that take place during evaporation of a liquid and condensation of a gas. **L1**

Class Activity: Water versus Alcohol

Simultaneously dab water and rubbing alcohol onto the board and have student infer the relative vapor pressures of the two liquids. **L2**

Use Visuals: Figure 13.12

Ask students what happens to vapor pressure of a liquid as temperature increases. **L2**

Differentiated Instruction: Gifted and Talented

Have students use Table 13.1 to create a linear plot of vapor pressure versus temperature. **L3**

Targeted Resources

❑ Small-Scale Chemistry Lab Manual: Lab 20
❑ GRSW: Section 13.2
❑ Transparency: 13.2 Connecting to Your World
❑ Transparency 143: Effect of Atmospheric Pressure on Boiling Temperature
❑ Transparency 144: Interpreting Graphs: Vapor Pressure–Temperature Diagram

3 ASSESS

Evaluate Understanding

Ask students to name some of the physical properties that distinguish a liquid from a gas. **L2**

Reteach

Remind students that the temperature at which vapor pressure of a liquid is equal to the atmospheric pressure is the boiling point of the liquid. **L1**

Targeted Resources

❑ Interactive Textbook with ChemASAP: Section 13.2

13.3 The Nature of Solids

2 Periods, 1 Block

Objectives

13.3.1 Explain how the way atoms are organized explains the properties of solids.

13.3.2 Identify the factors that determine the shape of a crystal.

13.3.3 Explain how allotropes of an element are different.

Vocabulary

melting point • crystal • unit cell • allotropes • amorphous solids • glasses

Ability Levels

L1 *Basic to Average*
L2 *For All Students*
L3 *Average to Advanced*

National Science Education Standards

B-2, B-5

---

1 FOCUS

Build Vocabulary

Explain the origin and meaning of the prefix and root for *amorphous*. Then have students list some amorphous objects. **L2**

---

2 INSTRUCT

Connecting to Your World
Discuss

Ask students to compare the structures of molecular and ionic compounds. **L2**

Use Visuals: Figure 13.14

Explain that the three-dimensional arrangement of particles in crystals is similar to the repetitive two-dimensional patterns found in wallpaper, tiles, and other decorative materials. **L1**

Teacher Demo: Crystalline Solid Model

Model a crystalline solid by placing an aqueous solution of detergent on an overhead projector and blowing bubbles into the solution. **L1**

Differentiated Instruction: Gifted and Talented

Have students write a short paper comparing the crystalline structure and formation of natural, synthetic, and simulated diamonds. **L3**

Relate

Ask students to research the different types of crystal structures that occur in nature. **L2**

Discuss

Ask students if they know of any elements besides carbon that exist in different allotropic forms. **L2**

Targeted Resources

❑ Laboratory Manual: Lab 21
❑ GRSW: Section 13.3
❑ Transparency: 13.3 Connecting to Your World
❑ Transparency 146: Crystal Systems
❑ Transparency 147: Cubic Lattices
❑ Go Online: Section 13.3

---

3 ASSESS

Evaluate Understanding

Have students describe the distinguishing characteristics of crystalline solids and amorphous solids. **L2**

Reteach

Describe what distinguishes solids from gases and liquids. **L1**

Targeted Resources

❑ Interactive Textbook with ChemASAP: Section 13.3

13.4 Changes of State

🕐 *2 Periods, 1 Block*

Objectives

13.4.1 Interpret the characteristics that a solid must have if it is to undergo sublimation at or near room temperature.

13.4.2 Describe how equilibrium conditions are represented in a phase diagram.

Vocabulary

phase diagram • triple point • sublimation

Ability Levels
L1 *Basic to Average*
L2 *For All Students*
L3 *Average to Advanced*

National Science Education Standards

A-1, A-2, B-2, B-3, E-2, G-1

1 FOCUS

Build Vocabulary

Ask students to predict the origin of the word *sublimation.* Then have them use a dictionary to determine the word's origin. **L2**

2 INSTRUCT

Connecting to Your World
Discuss

Stress that every substance has a unique set of properties that includes melting point, boiling point, and triple point. **L2**

Differentiated Instruction: Less Proficient Readers

Have students compare the pressure–temperature graph in Figure 13.12 to the graph in Figure 13.20. Ask students how many and which phases of each substance are being illustrated in Figure 13.12. **L1**

Use Visuals: Figure 13.20

Ask students to list the temperature and pressure at which the liquid and solid phases of water are in dynamic equilibrium. **L1**
Quick Lab: *Sublimation* **L2**

Targeted Resources

❏ Laboratory Manual: Lab 22
❏ Laboratory Practical: 13-1
❏ GRSW: Section 13.4
❏ Transparency: 13.4 Connecting to Your World
❏ Transparency 149: Interpreting Graphs: Phase Diagram of Water
❏ Go Online: Section 13.4

3 ASSESS

Evaluate Understanding

List a series of temperature–pressure values on the board. Then ask students to state which phase of water is most stable under each set of conditions. **L2**

Reteach

Draw an illustration representing ice, liquid water, and water vapor in equilibrium. Have volunteers add temperature labels for each phase and write an equation showing equilibrium. **L1**

Targeted Resources

❏ Interactive Textbook with ChemASAP: Section 13.4

14.1 Properties of Gases

⏲ *2 Periods, 1 Block*

Objectives

14.1.1 Explain why gases are easier to compress than solids or liquids are.

14.1.2 Describe the three factors that affect gas pressure.

Vocabulary
compressibility

Ability Levels
L1 *Basic to Average*
L2 *For All Students*
L3 *Average to Advanced*

National Science Education Standards
B-2, B-5

1 FOCUS

Build Vocabulary
Have each student define *compressibility* after they look up its prefix, root, and suffix. **L2**

2 INSTRUCT

Connecting to Your World
Relate
Discuss how the properties of gases lead to some unique uses of gases. **L2**

Differentiated Instruction: Special Needs
Have students construct a concept map to illustrate how the pressure of a contained gas changes when the amount of gas and the size of the container are changed. **L1**

Discuss
Ask questions about the proper use of an aerosol can and the purpose of the propellant. **L2**

Use Visuals: Figure 14.6
Point out that both visuals in Figure 14.6 have the same number of gas particles. Then ask why the pressure of a contained gas doubles when the volume is reduced by one-half. **L1**

Targeted Resources
❏ GRSW: Section 14.1
❏ Transparency: 14.1 Connecting to Your World
❏ Transparency 151: Gas Pressure and Volume
❏ Go Online: Section 14.1

3 ASSESS

Evaluate Understanding
Ask students how the following each affect the pressure of an enclosed gas: tripling the number of gas particles; doubling the volume; increasing temperature. **L2**

Reteach
Help students make a table to summarize how gas pressure changes as variables increase or decrease. **L1**

Targeted Resources
❏ Interactive Textbook with ChemASAP: Section 14.1

14.2 The Gas Laws

⟨⏱⟩ 2 Periods, 1 Block

Objectives
14.2.1 Describe the factors that determine physical properties of a liquid.
14.2.2 Use the combined gas law to solve problems.

Vocabulary
Boyle's law • Charles's law • Gay-Lussac's law • combined gas law

Ability Levels
L1 *Basic to Average*
L2 *For All Students*
L3 *Average to Advanced*

National Science Education Standards
A-1, A-2, B-2, B-5

1 FOCUS

Build Vocabulary
Have students create a concept map entitled "Gas Laws" to describe the vocabulary terms. **L2**

2 INSTRUCT

Connecting to Your World
Differentiated Instruction: Special Needs
Consider pairing students to solve the practice problems. **L1**

Differentiated Instruction: Gifted and Talented
Have students show that the numerical value of a in $V = V_0(1 + aT)$ is approximately $1/273$. **L3**

Relate
Have students discuss the relationships among gas pressure, average kinetic energy of gas particles, and Kelvin temperature. **L2**

Class Activity: Observing Pressure and Temperature of a Gas
Using hot and cold water, have students assess the firmness of an immersed bicycle tire to observe the relationship between pressure and temperature. **L2**

Discuss
After writing the combined gas law on the board, ask students what variable that is used to describe a gas is missing. **L2**

Targeted Resources
❑ Laboratory Manual: Labs 23, 24
❑ Laboratory Practical: 14-1, 14-2
❑ GRSW: Section 14.2
❑ Transparency: 14.2 Connecting to Your World
❑ Transparency 153: Interpreting Graphs: Boyle's Law and Charles's Law
❑ Transparency: Sample Problem 14.1: Using Boyle's Law
❑ Transparency: Sample Problem 14.2: Using Charles's Law
❑ Go Online: Section 14.2

3 ASSESS

Evaluate Understanding
Have students complete a temperature table that you start on the board. **L2**

Reteach
Mention how experiments subject a gas to both pressure and temperature changes that have opposite effects on volume. The combined gas law determines which variable has the greater effect on volume. **L1**

Targeted Resources
❑ Interactive Textbook with ChemASAP: Section 14.2

14.3 Ideal Gases

2 Periods, 1 Block

Objectives

14.3.1 Compute the value of an unknown variable in the equation for the ideal gas law.

14.3.2 Compare and contrast real and ideal gases.

Vocabulary

ideal gas constant • ideal gas law

Ability Levels

L1 Basic to Average
L2 For All Students
L3 Average to Advanced

National Science Education Standards

A-1, A-2, B-2

---

1 FOCUS

Build Vocabulary

Have students write a sentence or draw a concept map that explains the relationship between the two vocabulary terms. **L2**

---

2 INSTRUCT

Connecting to Your World

Discuss

Ask students how to determine the mass of a balloon full of helium gas at STP without making any mass measurements. **L2**

Discuss

Explain Avogadro's hypothesis. Start by pointing out how this hypothesis makes it possible to relate the molar quantity of a gas to its temperature, volume, and pressure. **L2**

Use Visuals: Figure 14.15

While students study Figure 14.15, point out all parts of the equation. Explain that the manipulated variable must be the volume. **L2**

Quick Lab: *Carbon Dioxide from Antacid Tablets* **L2**

Targeted Resources

❑ Probeware Lab Manual: Carbon Dioxide from Antacid Tablets

❑ GRSW: Section 14.3

❑ Transparency: 14.3 Connecting to Your World

❑ Transparency 157: Interpreting Graphs: Real Gases Deviate From the Ideal

---

3 ASSESS

Evaluate Understanding

Have students apply the ideal gas law to a sample of gas in a balloon. Ask them why a real gas can become a liquid, but an ideal gas cannot. **L2**

Reteach

Point out that the ideal gas law provides the number of moles of a gas by measuring its temperature, pressure, and volume. **L1**

Targeted Resources

❑ Interactive Textbook with ChemASAP: Section 14.3

14.4 Gases: Mixtures and Movements

2 Periods, 1 Block

Objectives

14.4.1 Relate the total pressure of a mixture of gases to the partial pressures of the component gases.

14.4.2 Explain how the molar mass of a gas affects the rate at which the gas diffuses and effuses.

Vocabulary

partial pressure • Dalton's law of partial pressures • diffusion • effusion • Graham's law of effusion

Ability Levels

L1 Basic to Average
L2 For All Students
L3 Average to Advanced

National Science Education Standards

A-1, A-2, B-2

---

1 FOCUS

Build Vocabulary

Ask students to use their own words to paraphrase the vocabulary definitions that they find in the section text. **L2**

---

2 INSTRUCT

Connecting to Your World
Discuss

Point out that the particles of each kind of gas in a mixture exert their own pressure as if they were by themselves. **L2**

Class Activity: Model Partial Pressure

Have students model Dalton's law by finding the mass of several groups of objects and comparing the sum of the mass of each group to the total mass of all the objects. **L2**

Differentiated Instruction: Special Needs

Have students write summaries of the chapter and share these with each other. **L1**

Use Visuals: Figure 14.18

Have students study Figure 14.18. Then explain to them that the diffusion rate is inversely proportional to the square root of the molar mass of the gas. **L2**

Targeted Resources

❑ Laboratory Manual: Lab 25
❑ Small-Scale Chemistry Lab Manual: Lab 21
❑ GRSW: Section 14.4
❑ Transparency: 14.4 Connecting to Your World
❑ Transparency 159: Dalton's Law of Partial Pressures
❑ Go Online: Section 14.4

---

3 ASSESS

Evaluate Understanding

Tell students that the partial pressures of oxygen and hydrogen gases in a container are both 100 kPa. Then ask them which has more molecules present and which has molecules with greater average kinetic energy. **L2**

Reteach

Point out the difference between diffusion and effusion. Remind students that Graham's law applies to both. **L1**

Targeted Resources

❑ Interactive Textbook with ChemASAP: Section 14.4

15.1 Water and Its Properties

2 Periods, 1 Block

Objectives

15.1.1 Explain the high surface tension and low vapor pressure of water in terms of the structure of the water molecules and hydrogen bonding.

15.1.2 Describe the structure of ice.

Vocabulary

surface tension • surfactant

Ability Levels

L1 *Basic to Average*
L2 *For All Students*
L3 *Average to Advanced*

National Science Education Standards

A-1, B-2

1 FOCUS

Build Vocabulary

Have students explain in their own words what the term *surfactant* means. **L2**

2 INSTRUCT

Connecting to Your World
Discuss

Tell students that most of Earth's water cannot be used by living organisms because it has a high concentration of salts. **L2**

Use Visuals: Figures 15.2 and 15.3

Have students discuss polarity and hydrogen boding while studying the figures. **L1**

Use Visuals: Figure 15.4

Use analogies to point out that the skin-like qualities of water are due to an exceptionally high surface tension. **L1**

For Enrichment

Have students design an experiment to determine the concentration of detergent at which water can no longer support the weight of a water strider. **L3**

Quick Lab: *Surfactants* **L2**

Targeted Resources

❏ GRSW: Section 15.1
❏ Transparency: 15.1 Connecting to Your World
❏ Transparency 161: Bond Polarities and Hydrogen Bonding

3 ASSESS

Evaluate Understanding

Ask students questions about surface tension to assess their understanding of how the molecular structure and chemical composition of water is related to its physical properties. **L2**

Reteach

Have students explain what property of water allows water's solid phase, ice, to float in its liquid phase. **L1**

Targeted Resources

❏ Interactive Textbook with ChemASAP: Section 15.1

15.2 Homogeneous Aqueous Systems

2 Periods, 1 Block

Objectives

15.2.1 Distinguish between a solvent and a solute.

15.2.2 Describe what happens in the solution process.

15.2.3 Explain why all ionic compounds are electrolytes.

15.2.4 Demonstrate how the formula for a hydrate is written.

Vocabulary

aqueous solution • solvent • solute • solvation • electrolyte • nonelectrolyte • strong electrolyte • weak electrolyte • hydrate

Ability Levels

L1 *Basic to Average*
L2 *For All Students*
L3 *Average to Advanced*

National Science Education Standards

A-1, B-2, G-1

1 FOCUS

Build Vocabulary

Have students make a concept map using the following terms: *salvation, solute, aqueous solution, solvent.* **L2**

2 INSTRUCT

Connecting to Your World
Discuss

Have students suggest memory aids to remind them of the definitions of *anion* and *cation*. **L2**

Use Visuals: Figure 15.7

Have students study the figure. Ask them questions to test their understanding. **L2**

Differentiated Instruction: Less Proficient Readers

Have students preview the section by looking for vocabulary and unfamiliar terms. **L1**

Teacher Demo: Electrolytes

Students will observe the testing of strong and weak electrolytes with a conductivity tester. **L2**

Targeted Resources

❏ Laboratory Manual: Labs 26, 27, 28, 29
❏ Small-Scale Chemistry Lab Manual: Labs 22, 23, 24
❏ Probeware Lab Manual: Electrolytes
❏ Laboratory Practical: 15-1
❏ GRSW: Section 15.2
❏ Transparency: 15.2 Connecting to Your World
❏ Transparency 163: Ionic Solid Dissolving
❏ Transparency: Sample Problem 15.1: Finding the Percent of Water in a Hydrate
❏ Go Online: Section 15.2

3 ASSESS

Evaluate Understanding

Ask students a series of questions to evaluate their understanding of the properties of aqueous solutions. **L2**

Reteach

Project models of water molecules, cations, and anions on an overhead projector. **L1**

Targeted Resources

❏ Interactive Textbook with ChemASAP: Section 15.2

15.3 Heterogeneous Aqueous Systems

2 Periods, 1 Block

Objectives

15.3.1 Distinguish between a suspension and a solution.

15.3.2 Identify the distinguishing characteristics of a colloid.

Vocabulary

suspension • colloid • Tyndall effect • Brownian motion • emulsion

Ability Levels

L1 *Basic to Average*
L2 *For All Students*
L3 *Average to Advanced*

National Science Education Standards

---

1 FOCUS

Build Vocabulary

Have students make a Venn diagram using the *terms solution, suspension, colloid, Tyndall effect,* and *Brownian motion.* **L2**

---

2 INSTRUCT

Connecting to Your World
Discuss

Refer the students to the feature on wastewater treatment. Explain how sedimentation and filtration play roles in the treatment process. **L2**

Use Visuals: Table 15.3

Use the table to help students understand the two part system of dispersed phase and continuous phase. **L1**

Differentiated Instruction: English Learners

Have students use a dictionary to look up the various uses of the word *disperse* or *dispersion.* **L2**

Relate

Bring examples of foods that are colloids or suspensions to class. Ask students to apply the criteria they have learned to determine the proper classification for these items. **L2**

Teacher Demo: Motion of Colloidal Particles

Demonstrate the Tyndall effect using a mixture of milk and water. **L2**

Relate

Discuss how fog is an example of a colloid and why drivers use low beams in fog. **L2**

Targeted Resources

❑ Small-Scale Chemistry Lab Manual: Lab 25
❑ GRSW: Section 15.3
❑ Transparency: 15.3 Connecting to Your World
❑ Transparency 167: The Tyndall Effect
❑ Transparency 168: Properties of Solutions, Colloids, and Suspensions
❑ Go Online: Section 15.3

---

3 ASSESS

Evaluate Understanding

Ask students to describe the ways that colloids are similar to solutions and to suspensions. **L2**

Reteach

Draw the relative sizes of spherical solute, colloid, and suspension particles on the board. Make an analogy to golf balls and ask questions that test students' understanding. **L1**

Targeted Resources

❑ Interactive Textbook with ChemASAP: Section 15.3

16.1 Properties of Solutions

⏱ *2 Periods, 1 Block*

Objectives

16.1.1 Identify the factors that determine the rate at which a solute dissolves.

16.1.2 Identify the units usually used to express the solubility of a solute.

16.1.3 Identify the factors that determine the mass of solute that will dissolve in a given mass of solute.

16.1.4 Calculate the solubility of a gas in a liquid under various pressure conditions.

Vocabulary

saturated solution • solubility • unsaturated solution • miscible • immiscible • supersaturated solution • Henry's law

Ability Levels
L1 *Basic to Average*
L2 *For All Students*
L3 *Average to Advanced*

National Science Education Standards
A-1, B-5, F-4, F-6

---

1 FOCUS

Build Vocabulary

Students can compare and contrast three types of solutions using a table. Include definitions and examples of each solution type. **L2**

---

2 INSTRUCT

Connecting to Your World
Relate

Prepare a bulletin board display using large pictures that illustrate the importance of solution processes in nature. Encourage students to contribute to the display. **L2**

Use Visuals: Figure 16.3

Have students study the figure and tell why the two liquids do not mix. **L2**

Differentiated Instruction: English Learners

Describe an analogy of a basketball game and compare this situation to equilibrium in a saturated solution. **L1**

Targeted Resources

❏ Laboratory Manual: Labs 30, 31
❏ Small-Scale Chemistry Lab Manual: Lab 26
❏ GRSW: Section 16.1
❏ Transparency: 16.1 Connecting to Your World
❏ Transparency 170: Interpreting Graphs: Solubility Varies with Temperature
❏ Go Online: Section 16.1

---

3 ASSESS

Evaluate Understanding

Have students use the concept of solvation to explain how agitation, temperature, and particle size affect the rate of solution formation. **L2**

Reteach

Review the factors that affect the aqueous solubilities of solid and gaseous substances. **L1**

Targeted Resources

❏ Interactive Textbook with ChemASAP: Section 16.1

16.2 Concentrations of Solutions

🕐 *2 Periods, 1 Block*

Objectives

16.2.1 Solve problems involving the molarity of a solution.

16.2.2 Describe the effect of dilution on the total moles of solute in solution.

16.2.3 Explain what is meant by percent by volume (% (v/v)) and percent by mass (% (m/m)) solutions.

Vocabulary

concentration • dilute solution • concentrated solution • molarity (*M*)

Ability Levels

L1 *Basic to Average*
L2 *For All Students*
L3 *Average to Advanced*

National Science Education Standards

A-1, A-2

---

1 FOCUS

Build Vocabulary

Students should make a web diagram using the terms *dilute solution, concentrated solution,* and *molarity,* and connecting them to the term *concentration.* **L2**

---

2 INSTRUCT

Connecting to Your World
Use Visuals: Figure 16.8

Explain that the sequence of steps is important when making up standard solutions because the solute plus the solvent will take up more volume than just the solvent alone. **L1**

Class Activity: Preparing Solutions

Demonstrate the correct method for preparing a one molar solution of a soluble compound. **L2**

Differentiated Instruction: Gifted and Talented

Have students write up steps for making an aqueous solution, imagining that they are writing a recipe for someone who does not know much about chemistry. **L3**

Teacher Demo: Serial Dilutions

Show students how to prepare several standard solutions with efficiency. **L2**

Targeted Resources

❏ Laboratory Manual: Lab 32
❏ Laboratory Practical: 16-1
❏ GRSW: Section 16.2
❏ Transparency: 16.2 Connecting to Your World
❏ Transparency: Sample Problem 16.2: Calculating the Molarity of a Solution
❏ Transparency 173: Concentrated and Dilute Solutions

---

3 ASSESS

Evaluate Understanding

Have students write out a numbered list of steps they would follow to prepare a solution. **L2**

Reteach

Remind students that using different measuring devices can affect accuracy when making dilute solutions. **L1**

Targeted Resources

❏ Interactive Textbook with ChemASAP: Section 16.2

16.3 Colligative Properties of Solutions

2 Periods, 1 Block

Objectives

16.3.1 Identify the three colligative properties of solutions.

16.3.2 Describe why the vapor pressure, freezing point, and boiling point of a solution differ from those properties of the pure solvent.

Vocabulary

colligative properties • freezing-point depression • boiling-point elevation

Ability Levels
L1 *Basic to Average*
L2 *For All Students*
L3 *Average to Advanced*

National Science Education Standards
A-1, A-2

1 FOCUS

Build Vocabulary

Students can rewrite the definitions of the vocabulary terms using their own words, including examples. **L2**

2 INSTRUCT

Connecting to Your World
Discuss

Remind students that ionic compounds and certain other compounds dissociate into two or more particles when they dissolve in water. **L2**

Use Visuals: Figure 16.15

Emphasize that colligative properties do not depend on the kind of particles, but on their concentration. **L1**

Class Activity: Freezing Point Depression

Students will observe the freezing point of ice change as rock salt is added to a slurry of ice water. **L2**

Quick Lab: *Solutions and Colloids* **L2**

Targeted Resources

❏ GRSW: Section 16.3
❏ Transparency: 16.3 Connecting to Your World
❏ Transparency 176: Particle Concentrations in Dissolved Compounds
❏ Go Online: Section 16.3

3 ASSESS

Evaluate Understanding

Have students explain how the addition of solute particles produces a lower vapor pressure, a higher boiling point, and a lower freezing point than those of the pure solvent. **L2**

Reteach

Remind students that colligative properties are those physical properties of solutions that depend only on the number of particles of solute in solution and not on the chemical composition of the particles. **L2**

Targeted Resources

❏ Interactive Textbook with ChemASAP: Section 16.3

16.4 Calculations Involving Colligative Properties

2 Periods, 1 Block

Objectives

16.4.1 Calculate the molality and mole fraction of a solution.

16.4.2 Describe how the freezing-point depression and boiling-point elevation are related to molality.

Vocabulary

molality (*m*) • mole fraction • molal boiling-point elevation constant (K_b) • molal freezing-point depression constant (K_f)

Ability Levels

L1 *Basic to Average*
L2 *For All Students*
L3 *Average to Advanced*

National Science Education Standards

A-1, A-2

1 FOCUS

Build Vocabulary

Use a chart to organize the definitions and the mathematical formulas associated with each vocabulary term. **L2**

2 INSTRUCT

Connecting to Your World
Use Visuals: Figure 16.18

Ask students to write down the definition of *molality* in their notebooks. Show the step-by-step approach a chemist would take to prepare a solution. **L1**

Discuss

Write the expressions defining molarity and molality on the board. Compare the chemical quantities in each expression. **L2**

Differentiated Instruction: Less Proficient Readers

Have students write sentences using the words *molarity* and *molality,* and have them circle the letter in each word that makes them distinct. **L1**

Class Activity: Diagramming Methods of Concentration Calculation

Students will design a diagram that describes and explains the various methods used to calculate the concentration of a solution. **L2**

Targeted Resources

❑ Laboratory Manual: Lab 33
❑ GRSW: Section 16.4
❑ Transparency: 16.4 Connecting to Your World
❑ Transparency 178: Interpreting Graphs: Vapor Pressure versus Temperature
❑ Transparency: Sample Problem 16.8: Calculating the Freezing Point Depression of a Solution

3 ASSESS

Evaluate Understanding

Ask students a series of questions to determine their understanding of boiling points and volatile compounds. **L2**

Reteach

Remind students that when they do calculations involving ionic solids they must find the molality of the solution in terms of the total number of particles. **L1**

Targeted Resources

❑ Interactive Textbook with ChemASAP: Section 16.4

17.1 The Flow of Energy—Heat and Work

2 Periods, 1 Block

Objectives

17.1.1 Explain the relationship between energy, heat, and work.

17.1.2 Distinguish between exothermic and endothermic processes.

17.1.3 Distinguish between heat capacity and specific heat.

Vocabulary

thermochemistry • chemical potential energy • heat • system • surroundings • law of conservation of energy • endothermic process • exothermic process • heat capacity • specific heat

Ability Levels

L1 *Basic to Average*
L2 *For All Students*
L3 *Average to Advanced*

National Science Education Standards

A-1, A-2, B-3, B-5

1 FOCUS

Build Vocabulary

Ask students to write a definition for each vocabulary term and use each in a sentence. **L2**

2 INSTRUCT

Connecting to Your World
Use Visuals: Figure 17.1

Have students explain what work is done as the chemical potential energy of the gasoline is released. **L1**

Teacher Demo: An Endothermic Reaction

Mix barium hydroxide octahydrate with ammonium chloride to show students an endothermic reaction between two solids. **L2**

Differentiated Instruction: Less Proficient Readers

Have students pay special attention to vocabulary terms that are defined by mathematical relationships. Encourage them to include example calculations along with their definitions of these terms. **L1**

Class Activity: Heat Transfer

Have students compare heat transfer of three different materials. **L2**

Targeted Resources

❑ Laboratory Manual: Lab 34
❑ Laboratory Practical: 17-1
❑ GRSW: Section 17.1
❑ Transparency: 17.1 Connecting to Your World
❑ Transparency: Conceptual Problem 17.1: Recognizing Exothermic and Endothermic Processes
❑ Transparency: Sample Problem 17.2: Calculating the Specific Heat of a Metal
❑ Go Online: Section 17.1

3 ASSESS

Evaluate Understanding

Have students discuss the flow of heat in two given different circumstances. **L2**

Reteach

Emphasize that substances vary in their response to an input of heat. **L1**

Targeted Resources

❑ Interactive Textbook with ChemASAP: Section 17.1

17.2 Measuring and Expressing Enthalpy Changes

2 Periods, 1 Block

Objectives

17.2.1 Construct equations that show the heat changes for chemical and physical processes.

17.2.2 Calculate heat changes in chemical and physical processes.

Vocabulary

calorimetry • calorimeter • enthalpy
• thermochemical equation • heat of reaction
• heat of combustion

Ability Levels

L1 *Basic to Average*
L2 *For All Students*
L3 *Average to Advanced*

National Science Education Standards
A-1, A-2, B-3, G-1

1 FOCUS

Build Vocabulary

Have students make a concept map using the vocabulary terms in this section. **L2**

2 INSTRUCT

Connecting to Your World
Class Activity: Calorimetry Measurements

Have students make calorimetry measurements and calculations. **L2**

Differentiated Instruction: Gifted and Talented

Have students evaluate whether or not the term *thermal pollution* is a literal description of the coolant water that comes from power plants. **L3**

Discuss

Discuss the use of calorimetry as an analytical tool. **L2**

Teacher Demo: An Exothermic Reaction

Show students an exothermic reaction and ask them to write a thermochemical equation to describe the reaction. **L2**

Targeted Resources

❏ Laboratory Manual: Labs 34, 35
❏ Laboratory Practical: 17-1, 17-2
❏ GRSW: Section 17.2
❏ Transparency: 17.2 Connecting to Your World
❏ Transparency: Sample Problem 17.3: Enthalpy Change in a Calorimetry Experiment
❏ Transparency 185: Enthalpy in Exothermic and Endothermic Reactions
❏ Transparency: Sample Problem 17.4: Using the Heat of Reaction to Calculate Enthalpy Change
❏ Go Online: Section 17.2

3 ASSESS

Evaluate Understanding

Have students communicate their knowledge about measuring and expressing heat changes. **L2**

Reteach

Write a thermochemical equation on the board and then draw the enthalpy diagram for the reaction. Remind students about the role of heat and total energy. **L1**

Targeted Resources

❏ Interactive Textbook with ChemASAP: Section 17.2

17.3 Heat in Changes of State

2 Periods, 1 Block

Objectives

17.3.1 Classify by type the heat changes that occur during melting, freezing, boiling, and condensing.

17.3.2 Calculate heat changes that occur during melting, freezing, boiling, and condensing.

Vocabulary

molar heat of fusion • molar heat of solidification • molar heat of vaporization • molar heat of condensation • molar heat of solution

Ability Levels

L1 Basic to Average
L2 For All Students
L3 Average to Advanced

National Science Education Standards

A-1, A-2, B-3

1 FOCUS

Build Vocabulary

After students read the vocabulary definitions, have them write a paragraph describing each term. **L2**

2 INSTRUCT

Connecting to Your World
Class Activity: Melting and Boiling

Have students measure the temperatures of boiling water and melting ice. **L2**

Use Visuals: Figure 17.11

Ask students if the process that occurs in a cold pack is endothermic or exothermic. Have them explain how they know this. **L1**

Quick Lab: *Heat of Fusion of Ice* **L2**

Targeted Resources

❏ Small-Scale Chemistry Lab Manual: Lab 27
❏ Probeware Lab Manual: Heat of Fusion of Ice
❏ GRSW: Section 17.3
❏ Transparency: 17.3 Connecting to Your World
❏ Transparency: Sample Problem 17.5: Using the Heat of Fusion in Phase Change Calculations
❏ Transparency 189: Interpreting Graphs: Heating Curve for Water

3 ASSESS

Evaluate Understanding

Ask students to sketch a heating curve for 1 mol of ice being heated from −10°C to 110°C. Then have them write a brief explanation of their graphs. **L2**

Reteach

Remind students that during endothermic phase changes, energy absorbed does not increase the temperature because the energy is being used to overcome attractions between particles. **L1**

Targeted Resources

❏ Interactive Textbook with ChemASAP: Section 17.3

17.4 Calculating Heats of Reaction

2 Periods, 1 Block

Objectives

17.4.1 Apply Hess's law of heat summation to find heat changes for chemical and physical processes.

17.4.2 Calculate heat changes using standard heats of formation.

Vocabulary

Hess's law of heat summation • standard heat of formation

Ability Levels

L1 *Basic to Average*
L2 *For All Students*
L3 *Average to Advanced*

National Science Education Standards

A-1, A-2, B-3

1 FOCUS

Build Vocabulary

Have students consider why Hess's law is called a law of heat summation. **L2**

2 INSTRUCT

Connecting to Your World
Use Visuals: Figure 17.13

After students study Figure 17.13, have them give the enthalpy change for the conversion of diamond to graphite. **L1**

Use Visuals: Figure 17.14

Ask students how they know that the formation of CO is exothermic in Figure 17.14. **L1**

Teacher Demo: Thermite Reaction

Have students observe the very exothermic thermite reaction. Then ask them to calculate the amount of heat released. **L2**

Targeted Resources

❏ Laboratory Manual: Lab 35
❏ Probeware Lab Manual: Heat of Combustion of a Candle
❏ Laboratory Practical: 17-2
❏ GRSW: Section 17.4
❏ Transparency: 17.4 Connecting to Your World
❏ Transparency 193: Standard Heats of Formation (ΔH_f^0) at 25°C and 101.3 kPa
❏ Transparency: Sample Problem 17.8: Calculating the Standard Heat of Reaction
❏ Transparency 195: Enthalpy Diagram
❏ Go Online: Section 17.4

3 ASSESS

Evaluate Understanding

Ask students to explain two ways that scientists can determine the heat of a reaction indirectly. **L2**

Reteach

On the board, work a heat-of-reaction problem using two indirect methods. **L1**

Targeted Resources

❏ Interactive Textbook with ChemASAP: Section 17.4

18.1 Rates of Reaction

2 Periods, 1 Block

Objectives

18.1.1 Describe how to express the rate of a chemical reaction.

18.1.2 Identify four factors that influence the rate of a chemical reaction.

Vocabulary

rate • collision theory • activation energy • activated complex • transition state • inhibitor

Ability Levels

L1 *Basic to Average*
L2 *For All Students*
L3 *Average to Advanced*

National Science Education Standards

A-1, A-2, B-3

1 FOCUS

Build Vocabulary

Have each student build a concept map of the vocabulary terms as they read the section. **L2**

2 INSTRUCT

Connecting to Your World
Discuss

Draw a chart on the board with columns labeled "very fast," "moderate," and "very slow." Ask students to suggest chemical changes for each category. **L2**

Differentiated Instruction: Special Needs

Create a model of colliding molecules to further explain the collision theory. **L1**

Differentiated Instruction: Gifted and Talented

Have students present to the class a report about typical reactions that require the collision of three or more particles. **L3**

Use Visuals: Figure 18.5

Explain that the diagram graphically depicts the energy changes that occur during a reaction. **L1**

Quick Lab: *Does Steel Burn?* **L2**

Targeted Resources

❑ Laboratory Manual: Labs 36, 37
❑ Small-Scale Chemistry Lab Manual: Lab 28
❑ Laboratory Practical: 18-1, 19-1
❑ GRSW: Section 18.1
❑ Transparency: 18.1 Connecting to Your World
❑ Transparency 197: Interpreting Graphs: Energy Changes in a Reaction
❑ Transparency 198: Interpreting Graphs: The Effect of a Catalyst on Activation Energy
❑ Go Online: Section 18.1

3 ASSESS

Evaluate Understanding

Have students use the activated complex theory to explain why hydrogen and oxygen do not react at room temperature but do combine explosively in the presence of a spark or flame. **L2**

Reteach

Use an analogy such as a crowded dance floor to discuss how temperature, pressure, and surface area affect the number of collisions in a reaction. **L1**

Targeted Resources

❑ Interactive Textbook with ChemASAP: Section 18.1

18.2 Reversible Reactions and Equilibrium

⏱ *2 Periods, 1 Block*

Objectives

18.2.1 Describe how the amounts of reactants and products change in a chemical system at equilibrium.

18.2.2 Identify three stresses that can change the equilibrium position of a chemical system.

18.2.3 Explain what the value of K_{eq} indicates about the position of equilibrium.

Vocabulary

reversible reaction • chemical equilibrium • equilibrium position • Le Châtelier's principle • equilibrium constant

Ability Levels
- **L1** *Basic to Average*
- **L2** *For All Students*
- **L3** *Average to Advanced*

National Science Education Standards
A-1, A-2, B-3

1 FOCUS

Build Vocabulary

Have students use the LINCS strategy to learn what Le Châtelier's principle means. **L2**

2 INSTRUCT

Connecting to Your World
Use Visuals: Figure 18.9

Explain that chemical reactions are often reversible. **L1**

Relate

Write the equation for the dissociation of H_2CO_3 on the board. Then explain how our bodies expel CO_2 to maintain the correct equilibrium between CO_2 and H_2CO_3. **L1**

Teacher Demo: Temperature Change and Equilibrium

Show students the effect of temperature changes on the equilibrium position of an exothermic reaction. **L2**

Discuss

Show students how to set up and solve problems involving equilibrium constants. **L2**

Targeted Resources

- ❑ Laboratory Manual: Lab 38
- ❑ Small-Scale Chemistry Lab Manual: Lab 29
- ❑ GRSW: Section 18.2
- ❑ Transparency: 18.2 Connecting to Your World
- ❑ Transparency 200: Interpreting Graphs: Changes in Concentrations of Reactants and Products
- ❑ Transparency: Sample Problem 18.2: Expressing and Calculating K_{eq}

3 ASSESS

Evaluate Understanding

Write several equilibrium chemical equations on the board and have students use Le Châtelier's principle to improve the yield of a reaction product. **L2**

Reteach

On the board list the steps for constructing an equilibrium expression. Use the equilibrium process for the production and decomposition of ozone in the stratosphere as an example. **L1**

Targeted Resources

- ❑ Interactive Textbook with ChemASAP: Section 18.2

18.3 Solubility Equilibrium

🕐 *2 Periods, 1 Block*

Objectives

18.3.1 Describe the relationship between the solubility product constant and the solubility of a compound.

18.3.2 Predict whether precipitation will occur when two salt solutions are mixed.

Vocabulary

solubility product constant • common ion • common ion effect

Ability Levels

L1 *Basic to Average*
L2 *For All Students*
L3 *Average to Advanced*

National Science Education Standards

A-1, A-2, B-2

1 FOCUS

Build Vocabulary

Make sure students know the difference between *solubility* and *solubility product.* **L2**

2 INSTRUCT

Connecting to Your World
Use Visuals: Table 18.1

Ask students if Table 18.1 helps them understand why barium sulfate can be used safely in humans for X-ray imaging. **L1**

Class Activity: Solubility Tables

Ask groups of students to create color-coded tables illustrating the solubilities of salts containing various anions. **L2**

Discuss

Point out that the common ion effect is an example of Le Châtelier's principle. **L2**

Relate

Explain how silver bromide on a film surface is involved in forming an image when film is developed. **L2**

Differentiated Instruction: Less Proficient Readers

Pair students so that a student struggling with word problems can work through practice problems with a student proficient at algebra and problem solving. **L1**

Targeted Resources

❏ Laboratory Manual: Lab 39
❏ GRSW: Section 18.3
❏ Transparency: 18.3 Connecting to Your World
❏ Transparency 204: Dissolving Silver Chloride
❏ Transparency 205: Solubilities of Ionic Compounds in Water
❏ Go Online: Section 18.3

3 ASSESS

Evaluate Understanding

Ask students to classify the salts in Table 18.2 on the basis of solubility. **L2**

Reteach

Review solubility product constants and solubilities and their relationship with each other. **L1**

Targeted Resources

❏ Interactive Textbook with ChemASAP: Section 18.3

18.4 Entropy and Free Energy

2 Periods, 1 Block

Objectives

18.4.1 Identify two characteristics of spontaneous reactions.

18.4.2 Describe the role of entropy in chemical reactions.

18.4.3 Identify two factors that determine the spontaneity of a reaction.

18.4.4 Define *Gibbs free-energy change.*

Vocabulary

free energy • spontaneous reaction
• nonspontaneous reaction • entropy • law of disorder • Gibbs free-energy change

Ability Levels
L1 *Basic to Average*
L2 *For All Students*
L3 *Average to Advanced*

National Science Education Standards

A-2, B-2, B-3, B-5

1 FOCUS

Build Vocabulary

Ask students to think about the meaning of *spontaneous* and *nonspontaneous* in relation to human behavior. **L2**

2 INSTRUCT

Connecting to Your World
Discuss

Discuss what is meant by *work.* Ask students if work is done on molecules when the temperature is raised or when chemical bonds are broken. Ask how energy is related to work. **L2**

Use Visuals: Figure 18.20

Explain that a fireworks display is a result of highly spontaneous reactions that release a large quantity of free energy. **L1**

Teacher Demo: Entropy and Water

Display a block of ice, a beaker of water, and a rapidly boiling beaker of water and ask students which item has the least entropy. Then ask which has the most entropy. **L2**

Differentiated Instruction: Gifted and Talented

Ask why the following reaction is spontaneous: iron, air, and water form rust with a negative value for the change in entropy. **L3**

Relate

Explain how the greenhouse effect is related to spontaneity. **L2**

Targeted Resources

❏ GRSW: Section 18.4
❏ Transparency: 18.4 Connecting to Your World
❏ Transparency 207: Entropy
❏ Transparency 208: Changes in Entropy
❏ Go Online: Section 18.4

3 ASSESS

Evaluate Understanding

Have pairs discuss the significance of positive and negative changes in entropy. **L2**

Reteach

Have students compare Table 18.3 and Figure 18.25 to review why some reactions are spontaneous and others are not. **L1**

Targeted Resources

❏ Interactive Textbook with ChemASAP: Section 18.4

18.5 The Progress of Chemical Reactions

2 Periods, 1 Block

Objectives

18.5.1 Describe the general relationship between the value of the specific rate constant, k, and the speed of a chemical reaction.

18.5.2 Interpret the hills and valleys in a reaction progress curve.

Vocabulary

rate law • specific rate constant • first-order reaction • elementary reaction • reaction mechanism • intermediate

Ability Levels

L1 *Basic to Average*
L2 *For All Students*
L3 *Average to Advanced*

National Science Education Standards

A-1, A-2, B-3, G-1, G-2

1 FOCUS

Build Vocabulary

Have students look up the prefix *inter* and the stem *mediate* in the dictionary, then define *intermediate* in their own words. **L2**

2 INSTRUCT

Connecting to Your World
Discuss

Initiate a discussion about how the effect of concentration on the reaction rate is expressed as a quantitative relationship. **L2**

Use Visuals: Figure 18.27

Explain the concept of slope. Then demonstrate how to calculate it. **L1**

Discuss

Tell students that in most cases reaction order cannot be predicted on the basis of a balanced equation; it must be determined experimentally. **L2**

Discuss

Explain that even complex reactions occur as a series of simple steps. Use the reaction between hydrogen and bromine as an example. **L2**

Targeted Resources

❏ GRSW: Section 18.5
❏ Transparency: 18.5 Connecting to Your World
❏ Transparency 210: Interpreting Graphs: The Rate of a First-Order Reaction
❏ Transparency: Conceptual Problem 18.2: Finding the Order of a Reaction from Experimental Data
❏ Transparency 212: Interpreting Graphs: Energy Changes for a Multi-Step Reaction
❏ Go Online: Section 18.5

3 ASSESS

Evaluate Understanding

Ask students to construct a reaction rate equation for the production of NO_2F from NO_2 and F_2. **L2**

Reteach

Remind students that many familiar reactions have multiple steps. **L1**

Targeted Resources

❏ Interactive Textbook with ChemASAP: Section 18.5

19.1 Acid-Base Theories

2 Periods, 1 Block

Objectives

19.1.1 Define the properties of acids and bases.

19.1.2 Compare and contrast acids and bases as defined by the theories of Arrhenius, Brønsted-Lowry, and Lewis.

Vocabulary

monoprotic acids • diprotic acids • triprotic acids • conjugate acid • conjugate base • conjugate acid-base pair • hydronium ion (H_3O^+) • amphoteric • Lewis acid • Lewis base

Ability Levels
L1 *Basic to Average*
L2 *For All Students*
L3 *Average to Advanced*

National Science Education Standards
A-1, B-3, G-2, G-3

1 FOCUS

Build Vocabulary
Have students think of words that use the prefixes *mono-*, *di-*, and *tri-*. **L2**

2 INSTRUCT

Connecting to Your World
Teacher Demo: Reactive Acids
Demonstrate a reaction between HCl and zinc that produces hydrogen gas. **L2**

Use Visuals: Table 19.1
Point out that the acids in Table 19.1 are listed in order of decreasing tendency to yield hydrogen ions. Ask what element they all have in common. **L1**

Discuss
Mention to students that acid–base concepts have been a part of chemistry for more than 300 years. Describe Arrhenius's theory. **L2**

Use Visuals: Table 19.3
Ask students to study the Brønsted-Lowry acid–base conjugate pairs in Table 19.3. Ask how hydrogen ions are related to these acids and bases. **L1**

Discuss
Inform students about the scientific importance of Lewis. Then describe how his theory of acids and bases was an extension of his concept of electron dot pairs. **L2**

Targeted Resources
❑ GRSW: Section 19.1
❑ Transparency: 19.1 Connecting to Your World
❑ Transparency: Conceptual Problem 19.1: Identifying Lewis Acids and Bases

3 ASSESS

Evaluate Understanding
Ask students to define *Arrhenius acids* and *Arrhenius bases* and to give an example of each. Have them show a given reaction can be treated as an acid-base reaction. Then, have them explain the Lewis theory. **L2**

Targeted Resources
❑ Interactive Textbook with ChemASAP: Section 19.1

19.2 Hydrogen Ions and Acidity

2 Periods, 1 Block

Objectives

19.2.1 Classify a solution as neutral, acidic, or basic, given the hydrogen-ion or hydroxide-ion concentration.

19.2.2 Convert hydrogen-ion concentrations into values of pH and hydroxide-ion concentrations into values of pOH.

19.2.3 Describe the purpose of pH indicators.

Vocabulary

self-ionization • neutral solution • ion-product constant for water (K_w) • acidic solution • basic solution • alkaline solutions • pH

Ability Levels
- **L1** *Basic to Average*
- **L2** *For All Students*
- **L3** *Average to Advanced*

National Science Education Standards
A-1, A-2, B-3

---

1 FOCUS

Build Vocabulary
Have students use a table to compare and contrast the properties of neutral, acid, basic, and alkaline solutions. **L2**

---

2 INSTRUCT

Connecting to Your World
Use Visuals: Figure 19.7
Have students examine Figure 19.7 and ask them which element is donating and which one is accepting a pair of electrons. **L1**

Differentiated Instruction: English Learners
Draw diagrams to help students visualize the relationship between hydrogen- and hydroxide-ion concentrations. **L2**

Differentiated Instruction: Gifted and Talented
Have students identify occupations in which people need to measure pH. Encourage them to interview a person with this job. **L3**

Teacher Demo: pH Indicators
Show students how pH indicators react to the acidity of their environment. **L2**

Relate
Point out that in the pH scale and in the Richter scale a change of one unit represents a tenfold change. **L2**

Quick Lab: *Indicators from Natural Sources* **L2**

Targeted Resources
- ❑ Laboratory Manual: Lab 40
- ❑ Small-Scale Chemistry Lab Manual: Lab 30
- ❑ Laboratory Practical: 19-2
- ❑ GRSW: Section 19.2
- ❑ Transparency: 19.2 Connecting to Your World
- ❑ Transparency 216: Self-Ionization of H_2O
- ❑ Transparency: Sample Problem 19.1: Finding the $[OH^-]$ of a Solution
- ❑ Transparency 222: Interpreting Graphs: Color Ranges of Acid–Base Indicators
- ❑ Go Online: Section 19.2

---

3 ASSESS

Evaluate Understanding
Have students use equations to describe the relationships learned in this section. **L2**

Targeted Resources
- ❑ Interactive Textbook with ChemASAP: Section 19.2

19.3 Strengths of Acids and Bases

 2 Periods, 1 Block

Objectives

19.3.1 Define *strong acids* and *weak acids*.

19.3.2 Calculate an acid dissociation constant (K_a) from concentration and pH measurements.

19.3.3 Order acids by strength according to their acid dissociation constants (K_a).

19.3.4 Order bases by strength according to their base dissociation constants (K_b).

Vocabulary

strong acids • weak acids • acid dissociation constant (K_a) • strong bases • weak bases • base dissociation constant (K_b)

Ability Levels

L1 *Basic to Average*
L2 *For All Students*
L3 *Average to Advanced*

National Science Education Standards

A-1, A-2, B-3, F-4, G-1

---

1 FOCUS

Build Vocabulary

Have students write each vocabulary word and its definition in a chart with headings *Acid* and *Base.* **L2**

---

2 INSTRUCT

Connecting to Your World
Use Visuals: Table 19.6

Ask which acid and which base is the weakest in Table 19.6. **L1**

Teacher Demo: Measuring pH

After dropping a different acid into two test tubes of sugar, ask students which acid is strong. **L2**

Class Activity: Shampoo Survey

Have groups compare shampoos for different hair types by testing the pH of each sample. **L1**

Discuss

Explain how the dissociation constant of an acid or base can be determined experimentally from the concentration of the solution and its pH. **L2**

Targeted Resources

❏ GRSW: Section 19.3
❏ Transparency: 19.3 Connecting to Your World
❏ Transparency: Sample Problem 19.5: Calculating a Dissociation Constant
❏ Go Online: Section 19.3

---

3 ASSESS

Evaluate Understanding

Ask students to list the two conditions needed to calculate the dissociation constant of a weak acid. **L2**

Reteach

Use an example to explain the information in Table 19.7. Have the class work together to list the steps for calculating dissociation constants. **L1**

Targeted Resources

❏ Interactive Textbook with ChemASAP: Section 19.3

19.4 Neutralization Reactions

2 Periods, 1 Block

Objectives

19.4.1 Explain how acid-base titration is used to calculate the concentration of an acid or a base.

19.4.2 Explain the concept of equivalence in neutralization reactions.

Vocabulary

neutralization reactions • equivalence point • standard solution • titration • end point

Ability Levels

L1 *Basic to Average*
L2 *For All Students*
L3 *Average to Advanced*

National Science Education Standards

A-1, A-2, B-3

1 FOCUS

Build Vocabulary

Have students create a table describing the relationship among the terms *standard solution, titration,* and *end point.* **L2**

2 INSTRUCT

Connecting to Your World
Discuss

Discuss what type of treatment is possible for cleaning up an acid spill. **L2**

Teacher Demo: Titration Using Indicators

Have students observe what happens when phenolphthalein is added to a NaOH solution and then HCl is added. **L2**

Discuss

Point out that neutralization is a process that occurs whenever an acid reacts with a base in the mole ratios specified by the balanced equation. **L2**

Use Visuals: Table 19.2 and Figure 19.20

Have students look at Table 19.2 and Figure 19.20 to find out what color will emerge when testing each of the following: household ammonia, lemon juice, seawater. **L1**

Teacher Demo: Titration Using a pH Meter

Students observe properties of the equivalence point. **L2**

Targeted Resources

❑ Laboratory Manual: Labs 41, 42, 43
❑ Small-Scale Chemistry Lab Manual: Lab 31
❑ Laboratory Practical: 19-2, 19-3
❑ GRSW: Section 19.4
❑ Transparency: 19.4 Connecting to Your World
❑ Transparency: Sample Problem 19.6: Finding the Number of Moles of an Acid in Neutralization

3 ASSESS

Evaluate Understanding

Have students summarize the titration process. **L2**

Reteach

Encourage students to use Figures 19.21 and 19.22 to describe to a partner how titration works. **L1**

Targeted Resources

❑ Interactive Textbook with ChemASAP: Section 19.4

19.5 Salts in Solution

⏱ *2 Periods, 1 Block*

Objectives

19.5.1 Define when a solution of a salt is acidic or basic.

19.5.2 Demonstrate with equations how buffers resist changes in pH.

Vocabulary

salt hydrolysis • buffers • buffer capacity

Ability Levels
L1 *Basic to Average*
L2 *For All Students*
L3 *Average to Advanced*

National Science Education Standards
A-1, B-3

---

1 FOCUS

Build Vocabulary
Ask students to look up the word *buffer* in the dictionary then define *buffer capacity* in their own words. **L2**

---

2 INSTRUCT

Connecting to Your World
Teacher Demo: Predicting pH of Solutions
Ask students to first predict the pH of different salt solutions, then check the pH of the solutions. **L2**

Use Visuals: Figures 19.22 and 19.25
Ask students to describe the difference between neutralization reactions that produce a neutral solution at the equivalence point and those that produce acidic or basic solutions. **L1**

Teacher Demo: Comparing Commerical Buffers
Compare antacid tablets, buffered aspirin, and aspirin to show that their neutralizing capacities differ. **L2**

Discuss
Explain how the limited dissociation of weak acids and bases gives these substances the ability to act as buffers. **L2**

Targeted Resources
❑ Laboratory Manual: Labs 44, 45
❑ Small-Scale Chemistry Lab Manual: Labs 32, 33
❑ GRSW: Section 19.5
❑ Transparency: 19.5 Connecting to Your World
❑ Transparency 228: Interpreting Graphs: Titrations of Weak Acid–Strong Base and Strong Acid–Strong Base
❑ Transparency 229: Using a pH Indicator

---

3 ASSESS

Evaluate Understanding
Have students explain what determines whether a solution containing a hydrolyzing salt is acidic or basic. Then ask them to explain how ethanoate ions can effectively remove hydrogen ions from solution. **L2**

Reteach
Use equations to show how the salt of a weak acid always reacts with water to produce hydroxide ions and the salt of a weak base always reacts to produce hydrogen ions. Remind students that chemical buffers are equilibrium systems that tend to resist change. **L1**

Targeted Resources
❑ Interactive Textbook with ChemASAP: Section 19.5

20.1 The Meaning of Oxidation and Reduction

2 Periods, 1 Block

Objectives

20.1.1 Define *oxidation* and *reduction* in terms of the loss or gain of oxygen or hydrogen and the loss or gain of electrons.

20.1.2 State the characteristics of a redox reaction, and **identify** the oxidizing agent and reducing agent.

Vocabulary

oxidation • reduction • oxidation–reduction reactions • redox reactions • reducing agent • oxidizing agent

Ability Levels

L1 *Basic to Average*
L2 *For All Students*
L3 *Average to Advanced*

National Science Education Standards

A-1, B-2, B-3

1 FOCUS

Build Vocabulary
Use a web diagram to connect this section's vocabulary terms. **L2**

2 INSTRUCT

Connecting to Your World
Teacher Demo: Oxidation and Reduction
Students observe how pure metals are obtained from their oxide ores by reduction. **L2**

Differentiated Instruction: Gifted and Talented
Have advanced students do research on redox reactions involving oxygen that are important in nature. **L3**

Class Activity: Identifying Oxidizing and Reducing Agents
Students write a reaction equation and identify the oxidizing and reducing agents. **L2**

Use Visuals: Figure 20.5
On the board, write the balanced redox reaction for hydrogen burning in oxygen. Identify the reducing and oxidizing agents and explain the identities based on loss or gain of electrons. **L1**

Targeted Resources
❏ Laboratory Manual: Lab 46
❏ Small-Scale Chemistry Lab Manual: Lab 34
❏ Laboratory Practical: 20-1
❏ GRSW: Section 20.1
❏ Transparency: 20.1 Connecting to Your World
❏ Transparency 231: Oxidation in a Bunsen Burner
❏ Transparency: Conceptual Problem 20.1: Identifying Oxidized and Reduced Reactants
❏ Transparency 233: Oxidation of Aluminum and Iron
❏ Go Online: Section 20.1

3 ASSESS

Evaluate Understanding
Ask students to identify the oxidizing and reducing agents of several redox reactions. Assess the logic that students use to arrive at their answers. **L2**

Reteach
To reinforce the dual nature of redox reactions, compare redox reactions to acid–base reactions. **L2**

Targeted Resources
❏ Interactive Textbook with ChemASAP: Section 20.1

20.2 Oxidation Numbers

⏱ *2 Periods, 1 Block*

Objectives

20.2.1 Determine the oxidation number of an atom of any element in a pure substance.

20.2.2 Define oxidation and reduction in terms of a change in oxidation number, and **identify** atoms being oxidized or reduced in redox reactions.

Vocabulary

oxidation number

Ability Levels

L1 *Basic to Average*
L2 *For All Students*
L3 *Average to Advanced*

National Science Education Standards

A-1, B-2, B-3

1 FOCUS

Build Vocabulary

Students can relate the vocabulary term *oxidation number* with other similar terms used in the chapter. **L2**

2 INSTRUCT

Connecting to Your World
Relate

Explain that determining oxidation numbers of elements in compounds is a way for chemists to keep track of electron transfer during redox reactions. **L2**

Teacher Demo: Redox Reactions

Students will observe a redox reaction and write a balanced equation describing it. **L2**

Differentiated Instruction: Gifted and Talented

Have students do research to discover why carbon monoxide is poisonous to living systems whereas carbon dioxide is relatively harmless. **L3**

Discuss

Lead a class discussion on determining oxidation numbers for elements in compounds by applying the rules for assigning oxidation numbers. **L2**

Class Activity: Assigning Oxidation Numbers

Students work cooperatively to assign oxidation numbers for various compounds. **L1**

Use Visuals: Figure 20.14

Have students study the figure and ask them what would happen if a copper nail were added to the solution instead. **L1**

Targeted Resources

❑ GRSW: Section 20.2
❑ Transparency: 20.2 Connecting to Your World
❑ Transparency: Conceptual Problem 20.2: Assigning Oxidation Numbers
❑ Transparency 236: Copper Metal Reacting with $AgNO_3$
❑ Transparency: Conceptual Problem 20.3: Identifying Elements Oxidized and Reduced
❑ Go Online: Section 20.2

3 ASSESS

Evaluate Understanding

Ask questions to determine students' understanding of oxidation and reduction reactions. **L2**

Reteach

Stress that oxidation numbers refer to the combining capacity of single atoms. **L1**

Targeted Resources

❑ Interactive Textbook with ChemASAP: Section 20.2

20.3 Balancing Redox Reactions

2 Periods, 1 Block

Objectives

20.3.1 **Balance** a redox equation by using the oxidation-number-change method.

20.3.2 **Balance** a redox equation by breaking a redox equation into oxidation and reduction half-reactions, and then using the half-reaction method.

Vocabulary

oxidation-number-change method • half-reaction • half-reaction method

Ability Levels
L1 *Basic to Average*
L2 *For All Students*
L3 *Average to Advanced*

National Science Education Standards
A-1, A-2, B-3, G-1

---

1 FOCUS

Build Vocabulary
Explain the meaning of the vocabulary terms using examples. **L2**

---

2 INSTRUCT

Connecting to Your World
Discuss
Ask students to recall the types of chemical reactions they studied in previous chapters. **L2**

Relate
Remind students of the concepts that underlie the need to balance equations. Ask students for other examples in which balancing is required to achieve conservation. **L2**

Differentiated Instruction: Less Proficient Readers
Working in small groups can help students who are easily frustrated to organize their efforts. Supervise the work closely to be sure each student is contributing. **L1**

Teacher Demo: Color Changes in Redox Reactions
Students will observe that redox reactions can sometimes be identified as a result of color changes. **L2**

Use Visuals: Table 20.2
Have students study the table and ask them to identify the oxidation numbers. **L1**

Targeted Resources
❑ Small-Scale Chemistry Lab Manual: Lab 35
❑ Probeware Lab Manual: Bleach It! Oxidize the Color Away
❑ GRSW: Section 20.3
❑ Transparency: 20.3 Connecting to Your World
❑ Transparency: Conceptual Problem 20.4: Identifying Redox Equations
❑ Transparency: Conceptual Problem 20.5: Balancing Redox Equations by Oxidation-Number Change
❑ Go Online: Section 20.3

---

3 ASSESS

Evaluate Understanding
Ask students questions to evaluate their understanding of different types of redox reactions. **L2**

Reteach
Point out that the distinguishing feature of redox reactions is the change in oxidation numbers that occurs. **L1**

Targeted Resources
❑ Interactive Textbook with ChemASAP: Section 20.3

21.1 Electrochemical Cells

4 Periods, 2 Blocks

Objectives

21.1.1 Use the activity series to **identify** which metal in a pair is more easily oxidized.

21.1.2 Identify the source of electrical energy in a voltaic cell.

21.1.3 Name a common portable source of electrical energy.

21.1.4 Describe the structure of a lead storage (car) battery.

21.1.5 Identify the overall reaction and product(s) of the hydrogen-oxygen fuel cell.

Ability Levels

L1 *Basic to Average*
L2 *For All Students*
L3 *Average to Advanced*

National Science Education Standards

B-3, E-2

Vocabulary

electrochemical process • electrochemical cell • voltaic cells • half-cell • salt bridge • electrode • anode • cathode • dry cell • battery • fuel cells

1 FOCUS

Build Vocabulary

Explain the Greek origins of *cathode* and *anode* and how these two words are related. **L2**

2 INSTRUCT

Connecting to Your World
Discuss

Explain how oxidation and reduction half-cell reactions are combined to form the net ionic equation for an electrochemical process. **L2**

Use Visuals: Figure 21.3

Explain that the reaction in Figure 21.3 could take place in a single beaker, but it would not be possible to produce a stream of electrons. **L1**

Teacher Demo: Inside a Dry Cell

Show students the construction of a dry cell and have them measure its voltage. **L1**

Relate

Have students research the use of fuel cells in the space shuttle and by utility companies. **L2**

Differentiated Instruction: Gifted and Talented

Have students research the current status of electric cars in the marketplace. They can write a report or prepare an oral presentation. **L3**

Targeted Resources

❏ Laboratory Manual: Lab 47
❏ Small-Scale Chemistry Lab Manual: Lab 36
❏ GRSW: Section 21.1
❏ Transparency: 21.1 Connecting to Your World
❏ Transparency 243: Activity Series of Metals, with Half-Reactions for Oxidation Process
❏ Go Online: Section 21.1

3 ASSESS

Evaluate Understanding

Have students sketch a tin/lead voltaic cell and label the cathode and anode. Ask them to write the equations for the half-reactions. **L2**

Reteach

Emphasize that a chemical reaction can produce a flow of electrons or a flow of electrons can cause a chemical reaction. **L1**

Targeted Resources

❏ Interactive Textbook with ChemASAP: Section 21.1

21.2 Half-Cells and Cell Potentials

4 Periods, 2 Blocks

Objectives
21.2.1 Identify the origin of the electrical potential of a cell.
21.2.2 Explain the value of the standard reduction potential of the hydrogen half-cell.
21.2.3 Describe how the standard reduction potential of a half-cell is determined.
21.2.4 Interpret the meaning of a positive standard cell potential.

Ability Levels
L1 *Basic to Average*
L2 *For All Students*
L3 *Average to Advanced*

National Science Education Standards
A-1, A-2, B-3
Vocabulary
electrical potential • reduction potential • cell potential • standard cell potential • standard hydrogen electrode

1 FOCUS

Build Vocabulary
Ask students to explain what a weather forecast means when there is a potential for rain. **L2**

2 INSTRUCT

Connecting to Your World
Discuss
Use the Celsius temperature scale as an analogy to explain the arbitrary assignment of 0.00 V to the hydrogen half-cell. **L2**
Teacher Demo: The Corrosion of Iron
Use pennies, metal wires, salt, water, and a paper towel to compare the galvanic corrosion of iron and compared. **L2**
Differentiated Instruction: Less Proficient Readers
Ask students to trace the movement of the electrons in Figure 21.10. Have them identify where oxidation and reduction take place. **L1**
Class Activity: Determining Cell Voltages
Have students work in groups to combine half-reactions using Table 21.2. **L2**

Differentiated Instruction: Gifted and Talented
Ask students to explain why large pieces of magnesium are attached to the hulls of ocean-going ships having steel (iron) hulls. **L3**

Targeted Resources
❑ Laboratory Manual: Lab 47
❑ GRSW: Section 21.2
❑ Transparency: 21.2 Connecting to Your World
❑ Transparency 247: Reduction Potentials at 25°C with 1*M* Concentrations of Aqueous Species
❑ Transparency: Sample Problem 21.1: Finding the Cell Reaction and the Standard Cell Potential
❑ Transparency: Conceptual Problem 21.2: Determining Reaction Spontaneity

3 ASSESS

Evaluate Understanding
Ask students to use Table 21.2 to create an electrochemical cell that will operate spontaneously. **L2**
Reteach
Write a nonspontaneous redox reaction on the board and ask students to name the element being reduced. **L1**

Targeted Resources
❑ Interactive Textbook with ChemASAP: Section 21.2

21.3 Electrolytic Cells

⏱ *2 Periods, 1 Block*

Objectives

21.3.1 Distinguish between electrolytic and voltaic cells.

21.3.2 Describe the process of electrolysis of water.

21.3.3 Identify the products of the electrolysis of water.

21.3.4 Name three processes in which the principles behind an electrolytic cell have been used.

Ability Levels
L1 *Basic to Average*
L2 *For All Students*
L3 *Average to Advanced*

National Science Education Standards

A-1, A-2, B-3

Vocabulary

electrolysis • electrolytic cell

1 FOCUS

Build Vocabulary

Have students name words, other than the ones in this section, that use *electr-* and *electro-*. **L2**

2 INSTRUCT

Connecting to Your World
Discuss

Ask students to describe what happens in a lead storage battery that provides immediate energy to start a car. **L2**

Teacher Demo: The Electrolysis of Water

Have students observe the electrolysis of water. **L2**

Differentiated Instruction: English Learners

Encourage students to review the chapter looking for the boldfaced vocabulary words. **L1**

Use Visuals: Figure 21.14

Ask students to explain the purpose of the battery in Figure 21.14. Then ask what substance is being oxidized in the electrolytic cell. **L1**

Relate

Discuss aspects of the Downs cell. Tell students that sodium is obtained by electrolysis of molten sodium chloride in the Downs cell. **L2**

Quick Lab: *Tarnish Removal* **L2**

Targeted Resources

❑ Laboratory Manual: Lab 48
❑ Laboratory Practical: 21-1
❑ GRSW: Section 21.3
❑ Transparency: 21.3 Connecting to Your World
❑ Transparency 251: Voltaic Cell and Electrolytic Cell
❑ Go Online: Section 21.3

3 ASSESS

Evaluate Understanding

Ask students to compare and contrast voltaic and electrolytic cells. **L2**

Reteach

Sketch a simple cell connected to a battery. Point out that the positive side of the battery is connected to the anode where oxidation takes place and that the negative side is connected to the cathode where reduction takes place. **L1**

Targeted Resources

❑ Interactive Textbook with ChemASAP: Section 21.3

22.1 Hydrocarbons

2 Periods, 1 Block

Objectives

22.1.1 Describe how many valence electrons carbon has and how many bonds it forms.
22.1.2 Define *alkanes*.
22.1.3 Identify which factors determine the solubility of hydrocarbons.

Vocabulary

hydrocarbons • alkanes • straight-chain alkanes • homologous series • condensed structureal formulas • substituent • alkyl group • branched-chain alkane

Ability Levels
L1 *Basic to Average*
L2 *For All Students*
L3 *Average to Advanced*

National Science Education Standards
A-1, A-2, B-2, G-1, G-2

1 FOCUS

Build Vocabulary
Have students define the vocabulary terms using their own words and giving examples. **L2**

2 INSTRUCT

Connecting to Your World
Teacher Demo: Methane's Shape
Construct models of methane, and ask students to explain why methane has a tetrahedral shape. **L2**

Differentiated Instruction: English Learners
Have students compile a glossary of the chapter in which they define each term in English and in their native language. **L1**

Discuss
Discuss how branched-chain alkanes differ from straight-chain alkanes. **L2**

Class Activity: Model of Ethane
Using molecular model sets, or foam balls and applicator sticks, have students construct a ball-and-stick model of ethane. **L2**

Targeted Resources
❑ GRSW: Section 22.1
❑ Transparency: 22.1 Connecting to Your World
❑ Transparency: Conceptual Problem 22.2: Naming Branched-Chain Alkanes
❑ Go Online: Section 22.1

3 ASSESS

Evaluate Understanding
Ask students several questions to assess their knowledge of alkanes. **L2**
Reteach
Quiz students orally to ensure memorization of the first ten prefixes use in hydrocarbon nomenclature. Then have students write the structural formulas for several compounds on the board. **L1**

Targeted Resources
❑ Interactive Textbook with ChemASAP: Section 22.1

22.2 Unsaturated Hydrocarbons

⏰ *2 Periods, 1 Block*

Objectives

22.2.1 Explain the difference between unsaturated and saturated hydrocarbons.

22.2.2 Differentiate between the structures of alkenes and alkynes.

Vocabulary

unsaturated compounds • saturated compounds • alkenes • alkynes

Ability Levels
L1 *Basic to Average*
L2 *For All Students*
L3 *Average to Advanced*

National Science Education Standards
B-2

1 FOCUS

Build Vocabulary

Have students use the vocabulary terms to create a compare/contrast table for unsaturated hydrocarbons and saturated hydrocarbons. **L2**

2 INSTRUCT

Connecting to Your World
Use Visuals: Figure 22.7

Have students compare the models of ethane and ethyne. **L1**

Class Activity: Double Bond Rigidity

Have students use their hands to model the rigidity of a double bond. **L1**

Targeted Resources

❑ GRSW: Section 22.2
❑ Transparency: 22.2 Connecting to Your World

3 ASSESS

Evaluate Understanding

Have students explain why compounds with double or triple bonds are called unsaturated compounds. **L2**

Reteach

Using molecular model sets, have students construct ball-and-stick models of ethane, ethane, and ethyne. Ask students to write the complete structural formula for each molecule. **L1**

Targeted Resources

❑ Interactive Textbook with ChemASAP: Section 22.2

22.3 Isomerism

2 Periods, 1 Block

Objectives

22.3.1 Distinguish between the physical and chemical properties of structural isomers.

22.3.2 Describe the conditions under which geometric isomerism is possible.

22.3.3 Identify the feature needed for two compounds of the same structural formula to be optical isomers.

Vocabulary

isomers • structural isomers • stereoisomers • geometric isomers • *trans* configuration • *cis* configuration • asymmetric carbon • optical isomers

Ability Levels
L1 *Basic to Average*
L2 *For All Students*
L3 *Average to Advanced*

National Science Education Standards

A-1, B-2, C-1

1 FOCUS

Build Vocabulary

To aid understanding of the term *isomer*, explain that it derives from Greek terms meaning "same parts." Have students identify another chemical term that begins with the prefix *iso-*. **L2**

2 INSTRUCT

Connecting to Your World
Class Activity: Modeling Isomers

Have students use models to construct the isomers of pentane and hexane. Have them draw the structural formulas for each isomer. **L2**

Discuss

Point out that the number of possible structural isomers for an alkane increases dramatically with increasing numbers of carbon atoms. **L2**

Use Visuals: Figure 22.10

Have students study the models. Tell them the key to the existence of stereoisomers is the presence of a carbon atom with four different groups attached to it. **L1**

Quick Lab: *Structural Isomers of Heptane* **L2**

Targeted Resources

❏ Small-Scale Chemistry Lab Manual: Lab 37
❏ GRSW: Section 22.3
❏ Transparency: 22.3 Connecting to Your World
❏ Transparency 258: Isomers

3 ASSESS

Evaluate Understanding

Have students explain what the term *isomer* means and then describe the differences between structural isomers, geometric isomers, and stereoisomers. Have them draw examples of each kind of isomer. **L2**

Reteach

Have students model *cis* and *trans* geometric isomers with their hands. Describe for them how the position of the thumbs creates both configurations. **L1**

Targeted Resources

❏ Interactive Textbook with ChemASAP: Section 22.3

22.4 Hydrocarbon Rings

2 Periods, 1 Block

Objectives
22.4.1 **Identify** common cyclic ring structures.
22.4.2 **Explain** resonance in terms of the aromatic ring of benzene.

Vocabulary
cyclic hydrocarbons • aliphatic hydrocarbons • arenes • aromatic compound • aliphatic compounds

Ability Levels
L1 *Basic to Average*
L2 *For All Students*
L3 *Average to Advanced*

National Science Education Standards
B-2

1 FOCUS

Build Vocabulary
Have students use the vocabulary words to create a web diagram showing how the different types of hydrocarbon rings relate. **L2**

2 INSTRUCT

Connecting to Your World
Use Visuals: Figure 22.11
Ask students why cycloohexane has two fewer hydrogen atoms than hexane. **L1**

Discuss
Students should be made aware that the formation of a ring causes bond strain in all cyclalkanes with rings that contain fewer than six carbons. **L2**

Targeted Resources
❑ Laboratory Manual: Lab 49
❑ Laboratory Practical: 22-1
❑ GRSW: Section 22.4
❑ Transparency: 22.4 Connecting to Your World
❑ Go Online: Section 22.4

3 ASSESS

Evaluate Understanding
Ask students to compare and contrast several terms as they relate to hydrocarbons. **L2**

Reteach
Review the terms *alkane, alkene, alkyne, cycloalkane, aliphatic,* and *aromatic.* **L1**

Targeted Resources
❑ Interactive Textbook with ChemASAP: Section 22.4

22.5 Hydrocarbons From Earth

⏰ *2 Periods, 1 Block*

Objectives

22.5.1 **Identify** three important fossil fuels and **describe** their origins.

22.5.2 **Describe** the composition of natural gas and coal.

22.5.3 **Describe** the first step in the refining of petroleum.

Vocabulary

cracking

Ability Levels
L1 *Basic to Average*
L2 *For All Students*
L3 *Average to Advanced*

National Science Education Standards

B-2

---

1 FOCUS

Build Vocabulary

Have students define *cracking* using their own words. **L2**

---

2 INSTRUCT

Connecting to Your World
Discuss

Describe the historical importance of petroleum. **L2**

Class Activity: Crude Oil

Divide the class into five groups and have each group create a display on one of the fractions obtained from crude oil. **L2**

Differentiated Instruction: Gifted and Talented

Have students research the energy sources used in the United States. Have them summarize their findings in a bar chart. **L3**

Targeted Resources

❑ GRSW: Section 22.5
❑ Transparency: 22.5 Connecting to Your World
❑ Transparency 261: Fractional Distillation
❑ Go Online: Section 22.5

---

3 ASSESS

Evaluate Understanding

Have students compare the formation of coal, natural gas, and petroleum. Have the students name some products made from natural gas, petroleum, and coal. **L2**

Reteach

Explain that petroleum is a complex mixture of hydrocarbons whose molecules range in size from 5 to 30 carbon atoms. **L1**

Targeted Resources

❑ Interactive Textbook with ChemASAP: Section 22.5

23.1 Introduction to Functional Groups

2 Periods, 1 Block

Objectives

23.1.1 Explain how organic compounds are classified.

23.1.2 Identify the IUPAC rules for naming halocarbons.

23.1.3 Describe how halocarbons can be prepared.

Vocabulary

functional group • halocarbons • alkyl halides • aryl halides • substitution reaction

Ability Levels
L1 *Basic to Average*
L2 *For All Students*
L3 *Average to Advanced*

National Science Education Standards
A-2, B-2, B-3

1 FOCUS

Build Vocabulary

Have students explain in their own words the meaning of the term *substitution reaction.* Explanations should include what is being substituted and what is being replaced. **L2**

2 INSTRUCT

Connecting to Your World
Discuss

Stress to students the importance that structure plays in the chemistry of organic molecules. **L2**

Use Visuals: Table 23.1

Have students study the table. Encourage them to memorize the general compound structure for each functional group. **L1**

Class Activity: Odors of Functional Groups

Students will experience the odors associated with several particular functional groups. **L2**

Differentiated Instruction: Gifted and Talented

Have students research examples in which the structure of a chemical plays an important role in a biological process. **L3**

Teacher Demo: Testing for Halocarbons

Students will observe the Beilstein test for determining the presence of halogen functionalities in organic compounds. **L2**

Targeted Resources

❑ GRSW: Section 23.1

❑ Transparency: 23.1 Connecting to Your World

❑ Transparency 263: Structural and Space-Filling Models of Hydrocarbons

❑ Transparency 264: Names of Some Common Alkyl Groups

❑ Go Online: Section 23.1

3 ASSESS

Evaluate Understanding

Write the structural formulas for ethane, ethyl chloride, and ethanol on the board. Ask students to name the compounds and identify their functional groups. **L2**

Reteach

Work with students to construct a concept map showing the connection between alkanes and their synthetic derivatives. **L1**

Targeted Resources

❑ Interactive Textbook with ChemASAP: Section 23.1

23.2 Alcohols and Ethers

2 Periods, 1 Block

Objectives

23.2.1 Identify how alcohols are classified and named.

23.2.2 Predict how the solubility of an alcohol varies with the length of its carbon chain.

23.2.3 Name the reactions of alkenes that may be used to introduce functional groups.

23.2.4 Construct the general structure of an ether and **describe** how ethers are named.

Ability Levels

L1 *Basic to Average*
L2 *For All Students*
L3 *Average to Advanced*

National Science Education Standards

B-2, B-3, G-2

Vocabulary

alcohol • hydroxyl group • fermentation • denatured alcohol • addition reaction • hydration reaction • hydrogenation reaction • ether

1 FOCUS

Build Vocabulary

To help students relate vocabulary to concepts discussed in this section, have them distinguish between *hydration* and *hydrogenation*. **L2**

2 INSTRUCT

Connecting to Your World
Discuss

Explain that alcohols and ethers are two important classes of organic compounds that contain oxygen. **L2**

Teacher Demo: Are Alcohols Basic?

Point out to students that, although they contain an –OH group, alcohols are not hydroxides. Test several alcohols with litmus paper to show that they have no basic properties. **L2**

Class Activity: Household Products with Alcohol

Bring some common household products that contain alcohols to class. Read the name of the alcohol given on each label and help students to write the structure for each alcohol. **L1**

Differentiated Instruction: Gifted and Talented

Have students design a simple experiment to show that fermentation can take place when the starting ingredient is table sugar (sucrose) instead of glucose. **L3**

Use Visuals: Figure 23.8

Ask students what they could conclude about the sample if the orange color remains. **L1**

Targeted Resources

❑ GRSW: Section 23.2
❑ Transparency: 23.2 Connecting to Your World
❑ Transparency 266: Alcohols Containing One, Two, or Three Hydroxyl Groups
❑ Go Online: Section 23.2

3 ASSESS

Evaluate Understanding

Have students draw the structural formulas for several alcohols and classify each as primary, secondary, or tertiary. **L2**

Reteach

Using reactions given in this section, point out that the two atoms being added can be identical or they can be different. **L1**

Targeted Resources

❑ Interactive Textbook with ChemASAP: Section 23.2

23.3 Carbonyl Compounds

4 Periods, 2 Blocks

Objectives

23.3.1 Identify the structure of a carbonyl group as found in aldehydes and ketones.

23.3.2 Construct the general formula for carboxylic acids and explain how they are named.

23.3.3 Describe an ester.

23.3.4 Explain how dehydration is an oxidation reaction.

Ability Levels
L1 *Basic to Average*
L2 *For All Students*
L3 *Average to Advanced*

National Science Education Standards

A-1, B-2, B-3

Vocabulary

carbonyl group • aldehyde • ketone • carboxylic acid • carboxyl group • fatty acids • esters • dehydrogenation reaction

1 FOCUS

Build Vocabulary

Use the following terms to make a concept map: *carbonyl group, aldehyde, ketone, carboxylic acid, carboxyl group, fatty acids.* **L2**

2 INSTRUCT

Connecting to Your World
Use Visuals: Table 23.4

Write several examples of aldehydes and ketones on the board and discuss the naming of these compounds. **L1**

Class Activity: Model Building

Have students make models of propanal, propanone, and propanoic acid. Have them compare their models. **L1**

Differentiated Instruction: Gifted and Talented

Have students consider how a carbonyl group next to an alkene group affects the stability of the molecule through resonance. **L3**

Discuss

Explain that many familiar smells and flavors come from organic compounds. **L2**

Quick Lab: *Testing for an Aldehyde* **L2**

Targeted Resources

❏ Laboratory Manual: Lab 50
❏ Small-Scale Chemistry Lab Manual: Labs 38, 39
❏ Laboratory Practical: 23-1
❏ GRSW: Section 23.3
❏ Transparency: 23.3 Connecting to Your World
❏ Transparency 269: Low Molar-Mass Carbonyl Compounds
❏ Go Online: Section 23.3

3 ASSESS

Evaluate Understanding

Write the molecular structures of vanillin, 3-heptanone, ethyl butanoate, and penanoic acid on the board. Have students classify each compound as an aldehyde, ketone, ester, or carboxylic acid. **L2**

Reteach

Review the oxidation states of carbon in organic compounds. Remind students that the oxidation state of carbon can cycle from –4 to +4. **L1**

Targeted Resources

❏ Interactive Textbook with ChemASAP: Section 23.3

23.4 Polymerization

🕐 *2 Periods, 1 Block*

Objectives

23.4.1 Describe how addition polymers are formed.

23.4.2 Describe how condensation polymers are formed.

Vocabulary

polymer • monomers

Ability Levels

L1 *Basic to Average*
L2 *For All Students*
L3 *Average to Advanced*

National Science Education Standards

B-2, B-3

1 FOCUS

Build Vocabulary

Explain the roots of the word *polymer* and describe examples of several polymers. **L2**

2 INSTRUCT

Connecting to Your World
Discuss

Discuss the similarities between the addition of hydrogen and halogens to alkenes and the formation of addition polymers. **L2**

Teacher Demo: Building a Polymer Model

Use a metal chain as a model for a polymer. Point out the features in the chain that are similar to a polymer molecule. **L1**

Differentiated Instruction: Less Proficient Readers

Have students collect several household items composed of different polymer materials. Ask students to create a table listing the items and the codes found on the bottom of each item. **L1**

Relate

Have students research the use of synthetic polymers in medicine. **L2**

Teacher Demo: Making Nylon

Demonstrate the synthesis of nylon for students. **L2**

Targeted Resources

❏ GRSW: Section 23.4
❏ Transparency: 23.4 Connecting to Your World
❏ Go Online: Section 23.4

3 ASSESS

Evaluate Understanding

Have students write sentences in their own words describing what takes place during the formation of a polymer. Ask students to describe the difference between an addition polymer and a condensation polymer. **L2**

Reteach

Remind students that the area of chemistry devoted to the study of polymers involves more than just plastics. To show how small changes in the structures of monomers can lead to dramatic differences in physical properties, compare polymers based on ethane and vinyl chloride. **L1**

Targeted Resources

❏ Interactive Textbook with ChemASAP: Section 23.4

24.1 A Strategy for Life

🕑 *2 Periods, 1 Block*

Objectives
24.1.1 Identify the fundamental units of life.
24.1.2 Describe how organisms get energy for their needs.

Vocabulary
photosynthesis

Ability Levels
L1 *Basic to Average*
L2 *For All Students*
L3 *Average to Advanced*

National Science Education Standards
C-1, C-3, C-4

1 FOCUS

Build Vocabulary
Explain the meanings of the different parts of the word *photosynthesis*. **L2**

2 INSTRUCT

Connecting to Your World
Use Visuals: Figure 24.1
Point out several key differences between eukaryotic cells and prokaryotic cells, including their sizes and metabolic reactions. **L1**

Class Activity: Living and NonLiving
Have teams of students create a list of characteristics that distinguish living from nonliving systems. **L2**

Relate
Explain the concept of carbon dioxide as a greenhouse gas and the concern that many scientists have about carbon dioxide being released into the atmosphere. **L2**

Targeted Resources
❑ GRSW: Section 24.1
❑ Transparency: 24.1 Connecting to Your World
❑ Transparency 272: Energy and Carbon Cycle
❑ Go Online: Section 24.1

3 ASSESS

Evaluate Understanding
Write the equation for photosynthesis on the board and ask the students questions about the reaction. **L2**

Reteach
Have students examine Figure 24.3. Point out that energy is required to maintain the highly organized chemical environments in living cells. **L1**

Targeted Resources
❑ Interactive Textbook with ChemASAP: Section 24.1

24.2 Carbohydrates

2 Periods, 1 Block

Objectives

24.2.1 **Describe** carbohydrates.
24.2.2 **Explain** how glucose polymers form.

Vocabulary

carbohydrates • monosaccharides
• disaccharide • polysaccharides

Ability Levels
L1 *Basic to Average*
L2 *For All Students*
L3 *Average to Advanced*

National Science Education Standards

B-2, C-1

---

1 FOCUS

Build Vocabulary

Make a concept map of the relationships among carbohydrates, monosaccharides, disaccharides, and polysaccharides. **L2**

---

2 INSTRUCT

Connecting to Your World
Using Visuals: Figure 24.4

Point out that plants are mostly composed of a carbohydrate known as cellulose. Ask students about the general formula for most carbohydrates. **L1**

Teacher Demo: Glucose and Fructose Models

Construct ball-and-stick models of glucose and fructose for students to examine while studying the molecular structures. **L2**

Teacher Demo: Benedict's Test

Use the Benedict's test to classify monosaccharides and polysaccharides. **L2**

Targeted Resources

❏ Small-Scale Chemistry Lab Manual: Lab 40
❏ GRSW: Section 24.2
❏ Transparency: 24.2 Connecting to Your World
❏ Transparency 274: Starch and Cellulose
❏ Go Online: Section 24.2

---

3 ASSESS

Evaluate Understanding

Have students describe the structure of monosaccharides, disaccharides and polysaccharides, and give a common example of each. **L2**

Reteach

Have students study the structures for the formation of sucrose. Ask them what happens in this condensation reaction. **L1**

Targeted Resources

❏ Interactive Textbook with ChemASAP: Section 24.2

24.3 Amino Acids and Their Polymers

2 Periods, 1 Block

Objectives
24.3.1 **Describe** the structure of an amino acid.

24.3.2 **Distinguish** between peptides and proteins.

24.3.3 **Explain** how enzymes affect biochemical reactions.

Vocabulary
amino acid • peptide • peptide bond • protein • enzymes • substrates • active site

Ability Levels

L1 *Basic to Average*
L2 *For All Students*
L3 *Average to Advanced*

National Science Education Standards
B-2, B-3, C-1

1 FOCUS

Build Vocabulary
Use a Venn diagram to compare peptides to proteins. Include the vocabulary for the section. **L2**

2 INSTRUCT

Connecting to Your World
Discuss
Discuss how to calculate the number of possible arrangements of amino acids in proteins. **L2**

Teacher Demo: Amino Acid Models
Use models to demonstrate how amino acids link through amide bonds to form peptides. **L2**

Differentiated Instruction: Gifted and Talented
Have students find out how the amino acid sequence of a protein dictates its secondary and tertiary structure. Ask them to draw a simple protein that shows some of the bonds affecting its shape. **L3**

Use Visuals: Figure 24.8
Compare the binding of a substrate and an enzyme to the way in which a key fits into a lock. **L1**

Relate
Discuss the importance of coenzymes in a proper diet. **L2**

Targeted Resources
❑ Small-Scale Chemistry Lab Manual: Lab 40
❑ GRSW: Section 24.3
❑ Transparency: 24.3 Connecting to Your World
❑ Transparency 276: Peptide Formations
❑ Transparency 277: Myoglobin
❑ Go Online: Section 24.3

3 ASSESS

Evaluate Understanding
Have students sketch the general structure of a tripeptide using letter abbreviations in place of the R group. Ask them to label the peptide bond and the carboxyl and amino ends. **L2**

Reteach
Use dryer duct tubing or slinky toys to help illustrate the secondary and tertiary structure of proteins. **L1**

Targeted Resources
❑ Interactive Textbook with ChemASAP: Section 24.3

24.4 Lipids

2 Periods, 1 Block

Objectives

24.4.1 Distinguish lipids from other classes of biological molecules.

24.4.2 Describe the structure of a lipid bilayer.

Vocabulary

lipids • triglyceride • saponification • phospholipids • waxes

Ability Levels

L1 *Basic to Average*
L2 *For All Students*
L3 *Average to Advanced*

National Science Education Standards

B-2, B-3, C-1

---

1 FOCUS

Build Vocabulary

Have students dissect the words *hydrophilic* and *hydrophobic*. Ask them for examples of other words that contain the same root. **L2**

---

2 INSTRUCT

Connecting to Your World
Discuss

Discuss why lipids are insoluble. Ask students questions concerning the characteristics of lipids. **L2**

Relate

Describe how lipid bilayers can assemble themselves without direction from DNA or RNA. **L2**

Differentiated Instruction: Special Needs

Create a model of a cell membrane by floating a layer of table-tennis balls in a tub of water. **L1**

Discuss

Point out that an important difference between waxes and oils is the length of the hydrocarbon backbone. **L2**

Targeted Resources

❑ Laboratory Manual: Lab 51
❑ Small-Scale Chemistry Lab Manual: Lab 40
❑ GRSW: Section 24.4
❑ Transparency: 24.4 Connecting to Your World
❑ Transparency 280: Cell Membrane
❑ Go Online: Section 24.4

---

3 ASSESS

Evaluate Understanding

Display samples of different types of lipids and ask students to decide what type they are, why they think so, and what that implies about their structure. **L2**

Reteach

Review the structures on pages 775–776. Point out that fats and oils hydrolyze in the presence of acids or bases because lipids are esters. **L1**

Targeted Resources

❑ Interactive Textbook with ChemASAP: Section 24.4

24.5 Nucleic Acids

⏱ *2 Periods, 1 Block*

Objectives

24.5.1 Identify the components of nucleic acids.

24.5.2 Explain how information is sorted in genetic material and how it can mutate.

24.5.3 Describe recombinant DNA technology.

Vocabulary

nucleic acids • nucleotides • gene

Ability Levels

L1 *Basic to Average*
L2 *For All Students*
L3 *Average to Advanced*

National Science Education Standards

A-1, A-2, C-1, C-2, C-3, F-6

1 FOCUS

Build Vocabulary

Give examples of how the root of many of the key words in this section relates to the nucleus of the cell. **L2**

2 INSTRUCT

Connecting to Your World
Relate

Have students read the autobiography of Nobel prize-winning chemist Arthur Kornberg. Encourage them to make a time line of the history of DNA. **L3**

Use Visuals: Figure 24.17

Point out the sequence complementarity between strands. Ask students about the experimental data concerning base-pairing. **L1**

Discuss

Have students critically examine the double helical structure by referring to the model built in the Quick Lab and the diagrams on page 779. **L2**

Differentiated Instruction: Gifted and Talented

Challenge students to write a computer program that converts any sequence of DNA bases into an amino acid sequence using the three-letter codes in Table 24.2. **L3**

Class Activity: Genetic Code

Have students practice reading the genetic code. Write a number of short DNA sequences on the board and ask students to translate the information into an amino acid sequence. **L2**

Targeted Resources

❏ GRSW: Section 24.5
❏ Transparency: 24.5 Connecting to Your World
❏ Transparency 282: Nucleotide Monomers of DNA
❏ Transparency 283: DNA Strands in a Double Helix
❏ Transparency 284: Three-Letter DNA Code Words for the Amino Acids
❏ Go Online: Section 24.5

3 ASSESS

Evaluate Understanding

Have students review the DNA models on pages 779–781 and write a short paragraph describing the structure of DNA. **L2**

Reteach

Display Figure 24.16 on an overhead projector. Use it to discuss the chemical and functional differences between DNA and RNA. **L1**

Targeted Resources

❏ Interactive Textbook with ChemASAP: Section 24.5

24.6 Metabolism

⏱ *2 Periods, 1 Block*

Objectives

24.6.1 Explain the function of ATP in the cell.

24.6.2 Distinguish between catabolism and anabolism.

24.6.3 Explain how nitrogen becomes available for organisms to use in synthesis.

Vocabulary

adenosine triphosphate • metabolism
• catabolism • anabolism

National Science Education Standards
A-2, B-3, C-1, C-4, C-5, F-4

---

1 FOCUS

Build Vocabulary

Have students write definitions of *metabolism, catabolism,* and *anabolism* in their own words. **L2**

---

2 INSTRUCT

Connecting to Your World
Discuss

Have students compare the free energy changes associated with spontaneous and nonspontaneous processes. **L2**

Relate

Explain how carbohydrates such as glycogen are utilized in the body. **L2**

Use Visuals: Figure 24.27

Discuss why there are no inputs that are not reflected in outputs. **L1**

Differentiated Instruction: Less Proficient Readers

Have students create cards for the steps in glucose breakdown. They can shuffle their cards and have another student put them in correct sequence. **L1**

Targeted Resources

❑ GRSW: Section 24.6
❑ Transparency: 24.6 Connecting to Your World
❑ Go Online: Section 24.6

---

3 ASSESS

Evaluate Understanding

Ask students to compare the carbon cycle to the nitrogen cycle. **L2**

Reteach

Draw a schematic diagram on the board that illustrates the exchange of energy between anabolic and catabolic reactions. **L1**

Targeted Resources

❑ Interactive Textbook with ChemASAP: Section 24.6

25.1 Nuclear Radiation

2 Periods, 1 Block

Objectives

25.1.1 Explain how an unstable nucleus releases
  energy.
25.1.2 Describe the three main types of nuclear
  radiation.

Vocabulary

radioisotopes • radioactivity • radiation • alpha
particle • beta particle • gamma ray

Ability Levels

L1 *Basic to Average*
L2 *For All Students*
L3 *Average to Advanced*

National Science Education Standards

B-1, B-3, G-3

1 FOCUS

Build Vocabulary

Have students look up the meanings of the first
three vocabulary terms. From these meanings,
have them infer the meaning of the prefix used
in all three terms. **L2**

2 INSTRUCT

Connecting to Your World
Discuss

Ask students a series of questions about atomic
structure. **L2**

Use Visuals: Table 25.1

Have students examine Table 25.1. Encourage
students to memorize the names and symbols
used to represent each type of radiation. **L1**

Teacher Demo: An Effect of Radiation

Use a key, a radiation source, and photographic
film to demonstrate the effects of radiation on
photographic film. **L2**

Relate

Have students discuss the differences between
gamma rays and other types of electromagnetic
radiation. **L2**

Targeted Resources

❏ GRSW: Section 25.1
❏ Transparency: 25.1 Connecting to Your World
❏ Transparency 287: Alpha, Beta, and Gamma
  Emission
❏ Transparency 288: Nuclear Decay

3 ASSESS

Evaluate Understanding

Write several partial equations for nuclear
decay. Have students compare the parent and
daughter nuclei to identify the type of particle
emitted. **L2**

Reteach

Remind students that when writing a nuclear
equation, the sums of the mass numbers and
atomic numbers of the reactants must equal the
sums of the mass and atomic numbers of the
products. **L1**

Targeted Resources

❏ Interactive Textbook with ChemASAP:
  Section 25.1

25.2 Nuclear Transformations

2 Periods, 1 Block

Objectives

25.2.1 Describe the type of decay a radioisotope undergoes.

25.2.2 Make calculations that involve half-life.

25.2.3 Explain the two ways transmutations can occur.

Vocabulary

band of stability • positron • half-life
• transmutation • transuranium elements

Ability Levels

L1 *Basic to Average*
L2 *For All Students*
L3 *Average to Advanced*

National Science Education Standards

A-1, B-1

1 FOCUS

Build Vocabulary

Have students look up the definitions of the vocabulary words and paraphrase each definition. **L2**

2 INSTRUCT

Connecting to Your World
Discuss

Explain that, for each element, there exists only a small range of neutron-to-proton ratios that produce stable nuclei. **L2**

Relate

Explain that the nuclear stability that results from a proper ratio of neutrons to protons in an atom is like the structural stability that results from a proper ratio of mortar to bricks in a building. **L2**

Use Visuals: Figure 25.5

After students examine the graph in Figure 25.5, have them consider the role neutrons play in stabilizing the nuclei of atoms. **L1**

Discuss

Emphasize that the rate of disintegration of the nuclei of an isotope is constant. **L2**

Differentiated Instruction: Less Proficient Readers

Have students who have difficulty reading draw inferences from tables and numbers. **L2**

Targeted Resources

❑ Small-Scale Chemistry Lab Manual: Lab 41
❑ GRSW: Section 25.2
❑ Transparency: 25.2 Connecting to Your World
❑ Transparency 290: Interpreting Graphs: Number of Neutrons vs. Number of Protons for Stable Nuclei
❑ Transparency: Sample Problem 25.1: Using Half-lives in Calculations
❑ Go Online: Section 25.2

3 ASSESS

Evaluate Understanding

Ask students how the ratio of neutrons to protons changes in nuclei that undergo beta particle and alpha particle emission. **L2**

Reteach

Point out the three natural processes that can result in a nucleus attaining a stable ratio of neutrons to protons. **L1**

Targeted Resources

❑ Interactive Textbook with ChemASAP: Section 25.2

25.3 Fission and Fusion of Atomic Nuclei

2 Periods, 1 Block

Objectives

25.3.1 Describe what happens in a nuclear chain reaction.

25.3.2 Explain the role of water in the storage of spent fuel rods.

25.3.3 Compare and contrast fission and fusion reactions.

Vocabulary

fission • neutron moderation • neutron absorption • fusion

Ability Levels

L1 *Basic to Average*
L2 *For All Students*
L3 *Average to Advanced*

National Science Education Standards

B-1, F-6

1 FOCUS

Build Vocabulary

Have students draw a concept map that correctly relates the vocabulary terms for this section. **L2**

2 INSTRUCT

Connecting to Your World
Teacher Demo: Model a Chain Reaction

Arrange matchsticks in a "Y" shape, and light the first one to demonstrate a chain reaction. **L2**

Use Visuals Figure 25.10

Display Figure 25.10 on an overhead projector and explain that uranium-235 does not spontaneously fission. **L1**

Differentiated Instruction: English Learners

Have students write definitions of fission and fusion in their native language and English. **L2**

Discuss

Explain that wastes produced in fission reactors contain isotopes with half-lives measured in thousands or hundreds of thousands of years. **L2**

Targeted Resources

❏ GRSW: Section 25.3
❏ Transparency: 25.3 Connecting to Your World

3 ASSESS

Evaluate Understanding

Ask students to write examples of nuclear equations describing nuclear fission and nuclear fusion. **L2**

Reteach

Explain that both nuclear fission and nuclear fusion produce energy by convection. **L1**

Targeted Resources

❏ Interactive Textbook with ChemASAP: Section 25.3

25.4 Radiation in Your Life

2 Periods, 1 Block

Objectives

25.4.1 Describe three devices that are used to detect radiation.

25.4.2 List examples of how radioisotopes are used in medicine.

Vocabulary

ionizing radiation • Geiger counter • scintillation counter • film badge • neutron activation analysis

Ability Levels
L1 *Basic to Average*
L2 *For All Students*
L3 *Average to Advanced*

National Science Education Standards

A-1, A-2, B-1, E-2, F-1

1 FOCUS

Build Vocabulary

Have students prepare a compare/contrast table using the different types of radiation detectors. **L2**

2 INSTRUCT

Connecting to Your World
Use Visuals: Figures on p. 817

Explain that a cloud chamber can be used to detect ionizing radiation. Ask students about other devices used to detect radiation. **L1**

Discuss

Explain that a Geiger counter is used to primarily detect beta radiation. Other forms of radiation are not easily detected. **L2**

Teacher Demo: Background Radiation

Use a Geiger counter to detect background radiation and discuss the sources. **L2**

Quick Lab: *Studying Inverse-Square Relationships* **L2**

Targeted Resources

❑ Laboratory Manual: Lab 52
❑ Probeware Lab Manual: Studying Inverse-Square Relationships
❑ Laboratory Practical: 25-1
❑ GRSW: Section 25.4
❑ Transparency: 25.4 Connecting to Your World
❑ Go Online: Section 25.4

3 ASSESS

Evaluate Understanding

Compare and contrast detection of radiation by a film badge and a scintillation counter. **L2**

Reteach

Explain that most smoke detectors work on the same principles as a radiation detector. **L1**

Targeted Resources

❑ Interactive Textbook with ChemASAP: Section 25.4